THE PRINTS OF
SAMUEL CHAMBERLAIN, N.A.

THE PRINTS OF
Samuel Chamberlain N.A.

DRYPOINTS · ETCHINGS · LITHOGRAPHS

by NARCISSA GELLATLY CHAMBERLAIN *and*
JANE FIELD KINGSLAND

WITH A FOREWORD BY PHILIP J. McNIFF
AND AN INTRODUCTION BY DAVID McCORD

BOSTON PUBLIC LIBRARY

1984

CONTENTS

THE PRINTS *continued*

PREFACE AND ACKNOWLEDGEMENTS

IN recent years, there has been a revival of interest in graphic artists who worked during the first half of the twentieth century. This renaissance has accentuated the need for a catalogue of the graphic work of Samuel Chamberlain, whose most productive years of printmaking were from 1924 to 1950. With the passage of time, memories dim, and records may be scattered or lost. The authors fortunately were able to begin their task of cataloguing Chamberlain's graphic work shortly after his death.

This book, as its title implies, confines itself to the artist's accomplishments in the print world. To those who recall the versatility of this prolific artist, the present volume will seem incomplete. However, the cataloguing of Chamberlain's hundreds of drawings in pencil, pen and ink, or other media, in addition to his more than seventy watercolors, could be the subject of an entire, separate volume. As well, a complete catalogue of his nearly sixty thousand photographic prints, many of which may be considered works of art in themselves, would fill several additional books. We are confident that our book *The Prints of Samuel Chamberlain, N.A.* establishes this artist's standing among graphic artists of his time, fulfills a need felt by collectors, dealers, museum curators, and students, and provides enjoyment for lovers of fine books.

The authors had been engaged for some time in the labor of researching and recording data on Chamberlain's prints when the idea of compiling and publishing a catalogue raisonné was suggested by Sinclair Hitchings, Keeper of Prints at the Boston Public Library. At that time, the artist's records and a nearly complete collection of his prints were available for study in his home and studio, but the largest source of research material was and continues to be the Boston Public Library, which owns copies of the artist's correspondence, records, books, portfolios, and other relevant publications, as well as many of the artist's drawings and graphic and photographic prints in its Wiggin Collection.

We indeed are fortunate that the happy collaboration between Director Philip McNiff, the staff of the Boston Public Library, and Samuel Chamberlain, which in 1968 culminated in the publication of the autobiographical book *Etched in Sunlight*, could be repeated to produce this book with the artist's widow, Narcissa Gellatly Chamberlain, and co-author, Jane Field Kingsland.

A volume containing as great a number of detailed facts as this one does could not have been written without the help of many individuals in diverse occupations. To all of them, we acknowledge our indebtedness.

First and foremost, we wish to acknowledge our gratitude to Sinclair Hamilton Hitchings, without whose friendly urging, gentle coaching, and continuing help this book never would have been undertaken, let alone brought to completion. He has guided us throughout the task of ordering quantities of data into a structure that we hope will facilitate the use of this catalogue raisonné.

The authors are indebted to Charles D. Childs for having had the foresight to keep many of the artist's letters and for having deposited them at the Boston Public Library. Childs' own writings have been invaluable to us for verifying dates and other facts about the publication of many of Chamberlain's early prints.

Others to whom we are deeply indebted include June and Norman Kraeft of June 1 Gallery, Bethlehem, Connecticut. In addition to providing us with the only proof we have seen of print No. 22, *Rue Daubenton*, and giving us permission to reprint their essay from The Octagon catalogue of the memorial exhibition of Samuel Chamberlain's drawings and prints, they have contributed generously from their wealth of detailed information about the printing and publishing of many of Chamberlain's prints. We are grateful also to Walter Frese, President of Hastings House Publishers of New York, for verifying publication data and helping us find a proof of print No. 255, *A Windmill*.

A special debt of gratitude is acknowledged to John Ivar Lund and his company, Iconographics, for photographic chores and assistance with typing as well as for converting the measurements of the prints from the English system to the metric. Mr. Lund's wife, the co-author, Jane Kingsland, wishes to thank him for his sustained encouragement during the years of labor required to prepare this work for publication.

We wish to extend our heartfelt thanks to Mary Ellen Branscombe, who typed a considerable portion of this work and verified many details of research from many sources.

Gratitude is extended to Mrs. Jeanne Butler, formerly of the American Institute of Architects Foundation at The Octagon, Washington, D.C., for her kind permission to reprint the four essays that were written for the catalogue of the memorial exhibition of drawings and prints of Samuel Chamberlain, held at The Octagon in September and October of 1975. Mrs. Walter Muir Whitehill also has allowed us to reprint her late husband's essay, one of the four referred to above, as have Sinclair Hitchings and June and Norman Kraeft.

We are indebted to John W. Rafferty of Topsfield, Massachusetts, who patiently read each of many drafts of the section "A Guide to the Prints" and made careful suggestions for clarifying meaning.

We thank Theresa D. Cedarholm of the Fine Arts Department at the Boston Public Library for finding copies of the magazine articles by Samuel Chamberlain that are reprinted here.

Our thanks are offered to the following people for helping to identify the correct location of the Memorial Chapel that is the subject of print No. 285 and had been inaccurately listed in the artist's records: James C. Kelly, Chief Researcher at the Tennessee State Museum, Nashville,

Tennessee; Winthrop G. Morrison, Registrar and Director of the Division of Academic Services, University of Louisville, Kentucky; Marguerite C. Wakefield of Crestwood, Kentucky; and Wilson Bryant, Superintendent of the Duncan Memorial Chapel and Gardens, Crestwood, Kentucky.

Gratitude is due to the following people for contributing accurate information about the location and identity of prints by Samuel Chamberlain in museums and other public institutions: Marcia A. Aquino of the Department of Prints and Drawings, The Cleveland Museum of Art, Cleveland, Ohio; Ellen Buie, McDermot Intern, The Dallas Museum of Fine Arts, Dallas, Texas; Jane Darnell, Volunteer Researcher, The New Britain Museum of American Art, New Britain, Connecticut; Mary Lou DeLapp, Print Cataloguer, The Huntington Library, San Marino, California; Ebria Feinblatt, Senior Curator, Prints and Drawings Department, Los Angeles County Museum of Art, Los Angeles, California; Norman A. Geska, Director, Sheldon Memorial Art Galleries, University of Nebraska-Lincoln, Lincoln, Nebraska; Betty Keen, Registrar of The Birmingham Museum of Art, Birmingham, Alabama; Nancy Kemper of The Norton Simon Museum of Art, Pasadena, California; Aida El-Khalidi, Assistant to the Registrar, University of Michigan Museum of Art, Ann Arbor, Michigan; J. Stanley Mullin of Los Angeles, California; Eva Mosely, Curator of Manuscripts, The Arthur and Elizabeth Schlesinger Library of Women in America, Radcliffe College, Cambridge, Massachusetts; Henry Riely, Registration Aide, The Wadsworth Atheneum, Hartford, Connecticut; Deborah A. Stavin, Assistant Registrar of The William Rockhill Nelson Gallery of Art, Atkins Museum of Fine Arts, Kansas City, Missouri; Nicki Thiras, Assistant to the Director, Addison Gallery of American Art, Phillips Academy, Andover, Massachusetts; Judith Weiss, Kress Fellow in Prints, The Toledo Museum of Art, Toledo, Ohio; James M. Wiley, Curatorial Assistant, Modern Art Department, Seattle Art Museum, Seattle, Washington; and John M. Wisdom, Curator of Painting and Sculpture, Museum of Fine Arts, Houston, Texas.

We acknowledge our indebtedness to The Arthur and Elizabeth Schlesinger Library of the History of Women in America for providing us with data about print No. 200, *Lydia Pinkham Compound Label*, and we thank Ted Polumbaum, photographer for *Life* magazine, for the use of his photograph taken of Samuel Chamberlain in 1960.

We wish to record our heartfelt thanks to David McCord for his gracious introduction to all that follows.

N.G.C. AND J.F.K.

FOREWORD

THE Boston Public Library's long and happy association with the Chamberlain family began in 1960 with purchases of a number of Samuel Chamberlain's drypoints, etchings, and lithographs, and in 1961 with an exhibition of these prints in the Library's Wiggin Gallery. In 1966 the Library commissioned an autobiography by Samuel Chamberlain, published in 1968 under the title *Etched in Sunlight* and subtitled *Fifty Years in the Graphic Arts*. A second Wiggin Gallery exhibition of his prints celebrated publication of the book. An exhibition of his photographs, drawn from the Library's collections, was held in the Wiggin Gallery in 1978. Thanks in part to gifts from Mrs. Chamberlain, the Library has come to own the largest public collection of Chamberlain's prints, drawings, photographs, and books. In 1984 we are happy to publish the present volume by Mrs. Chamberlain and Jane Field Kingsland.

The Prints of Samuel Chamberlain, N.A., became possible through their efforts and through gifts from friends. As a definitive reference and a salute to an accomplished and delightful man, the book has required a large investment of time and money. We extend heartfelt thanks to all who made contributions toward the expense of such a project in which high quality has been sought through painstaking effort.

Particular thanks are due to Charles D. Childs, for many years the Library's Honorary Keeper of Prints. As a member of the Print Department of Goodspeed's Book Shop, in 1927, Mr. Childs wrote the first monograph of the prints of Samuel Chamberlain. His friendship with the Chamberlain family has continued ever since. The Boston Public Library likewise continues to receive his interest, encouragement and good will. The present large volume has a forerunner in his slim bound volume, an essay and listing of prints, published almost sixty years ago.

PHILIP J. MCNIFF
Director Emeritus
Boston Public Library

4

INTRODUCTION

M Y EARLIEST IMPRESSION of Samuel Chamberlain—*impression* of course is an etcher's word—was not of him as an etcher. I had, as I remember the year 1926 or 1927, never heard of him. But in Goodspeed's Book Shop, then located in Ashburton Place, Boston, I discovered and bought for fifteen dollars a small micro-perfect pencil drawing, signed "Samuel Chamberlain: Ravello." It was undated; but I have since learned that he undoubtedly made the drawing—really a vignette and in no way simply a sketch—on one of his earliest, perhaps his first, of Italian journeys. Today that drawing hangs, distilled under glass, in front of me.

As I look at the sentence above, I suddenly realize how entangled in the vast web of this remarkable artist's work and interests I have become. I chose the word "distilled" hastily (and wrongly) as reflecting Chamberlain's interest in, and expert knowledge of, the vineyards of France. Of course it suggests not France but the Scotland of his fellow etchers—Bone, Cameron, and McBey. But geography aside, I choose it still as the word for Chamberlain's draughtsmanship in pencil.

My delight in the Ravello drawing remains undiminished. Let me quote a tiny passage from J. B. Priestley's *English Journey*. I regret that I never quoted this to Sam Chamberlain himself. It would have pleased him deep down under his honest modesty to know how some people respond to a work of genius. "They have here," said Mr. Priestley, speaking of a watercolor in the Art Gallery in Birmingham, "a little harvest scene by de Windt—a tiny wagon or two, then a glorious melting distance of rolling country and sky—that I should like somebody to steal for me. It lit up my morning. All the years between Peter de Windt and myself were annihilated in a flash; he pointed and I saw, he spoke and I heard; and his mood, felt on that autumn day long ago, was mine."

Samuel Chamberlain, N.A., was an enchanting man to meet and to know. Look carefully at the frontispiece photograph of him—to the left of where you are—taken by Ted Polumbaum, a *Life* photographer. Does it seem to you *consciously* posed? It is not. From the magic of that smile, from the kindliness so evident in this so obvious host; from the background atmosphere of kitchen utensils and the foreground of sartorial correctness, can you possibly deduce the relentless drive, the many splendid talents and central genius of the artist? Photographs of artists—the

5

man at his easel, the modern sculptor amid his clutter of metal, broken-down machinery, and welding blow torch—don't resolve into anything like this. Don't fool yourself. You are looking at the perfectionist in culinary art and vineyard matters. The photographer *in* Chamberlain—not the photographer *of* Chamberlain—chose the background. Has the very aroma of the kitchen escaped you? *Kleider machen Leute?* The late J. D. Constable, great connoisseur of art, told me in a forgotten *Harper's* essay, what Baedeker must have looked like physically, based solely on personal idiosyncrasies revealed in his famous Guide Books. Here we have the reverse. Banesh Hoffmann, in his introduction to the sixth revised edition of Edwin A. Abbott's extraordinary little book (Dover) called *Flatland*, asks the question I am asking about Chamberlain. To write such a book ahead of Einstein (brief and for the layman) one would think that Abbott must have been a mathematician or a physicist. He was neither. He was a headmaster of a school; the classics his field. "Does this sound like the sort of man," asks Mr. Hoffmann, "who would write an absorbing mathematical adventure?"—which it certainly is.

I say all this simply to prepare the reader for the uninterrupted delight of Chamberlain's three essays on the workmanship and procedure in making an etching, a lithograph, and a drypoint. These three expository pieces belong *in toto* to the smiling, modest man of the photograph. They are in simplicity unstudied the work of a very private man. What a belated introduction they provide for that monumental volume, *Etched in Sunlight* (1968): architect, artist with a pencil, etcher, lithographer, master of drypoint; ingenious photographer of old houses and curious buildings inside out; traveller, graphic historian; expert on French cooking; vintner at your dining table. Yet somehow all—every one—of these related yet disparate disciplines seem completely natural to the late subject of the Polumbaum photograph, always far too busy to be unrelaxed—a gift the gods bestow on precious few. Hard-working and in love with his work makes a man more loveable for a kind of sui-generis generosity of spirit quite impossible to conceal.

These three essays of course are not the *raison d'être* of *The Prints of Samuel Chamberlain, N.A.*, published as a definitive catalogue of Chamberlain's etchings, drypoints, and lithographs. Yet, if you can manage to read them slowly and thoughtfully, you will find that they seem visibly to isolate themselves, like frogs on a lily pad. Laymen concerned with art won't fail to enjoy them. But the ideal reader will always be the architect in his transition phase, if indeed he yearns to *make* the transition (as Gardner Cox, for example, has done) from the T-square to the burin or the brush. To any and all such these three little essays will surely seem as important as Strunk and E. B. White's *Elements of Style*, or F. L. Lucas's bilingual masterpiece called *Style*, are to the beginning writer. So deceptively simple are Chamberlain's essays that but one word in them—*poncif*—could be considered unknown by the intelligent layman. The congenital collector remembers such a new (to him) word when used this way *in isolation*! *dissentient* in *The Good Companions*; *iridule* and *lemniscate* in Nabokov's *Pale Fire*; *enthymeme* in *The Vicar of Wakefield*. And he remembers them in the way that J. Bronowski was to find them in Newton's work of "destiny in simplicity." Sam Chamberlain loved the world; and his vision, or so it seems to me, was in Samuel Eliot Morison's view (applied to the historian): "His vision should be vertical, not horizontal: down to the roots, up toward the stars."

Perhaps for some good reason none of Chamberlain's critics, editors, publishers, nor any of his far from aloof admirers have openly observed how this man, well travelled in high places, in crowds, in solitude, in lonely country, and sometimes in a lonelier city—for all the *bon vivant* that he was—has brought not only to his drawings, etchings, lithographs, drypoints, and most especially to his enormous flock of popular photographic books what the sailors, especially those who sailed in square-rig, called "The Great Silence": the silence honoring the 11 November 1918 Armistice so movingly described by Alexander H. Bone, youngest brother of Sir Muirhead the etcher, in a book called *Bowsprit Ashore* (Jonathan Cape, 1932). "I have been told many stories of the great silence by seamen friends, but the one that appeals to me most was from a first-voyage third officer who had just completed his time in sail. The ship in which he had served his time had been one of the last square-rigged vessels under the British flag. She had been at sea on two November elevenths, and on both occasions the captain had brought his ship to the wind and backed the mainyards, a manoeuvre similar to stopping the engines on a steamer. But there they would not have had the silence one could get on a steamer. There would have been the noise of strained stay or swifter; the flap of a sail against a shroud; the never-ceasing noises of a tall ship. But the scene would have been more impressive and solemn to the heart and mind of a sailorman. I can picture it truly, as I've been present at a similar sight when a grey-haired old mariner heaved his ship to, and kept a silence of his own over the spot where his son had been lost at sea."

I think Sam Chamberlain truly understood and reverenced the essential great silence of the world that man has lost now even at sea; more recently in the air, though perhaps not yet on the desert, in the Grand Canyon, in what's left of the wilderness. It is still what the fisherman seeks; and the monk, the Buddhist, the human needles of India swung or swinging toward Mecca. It is there in the Taj Mahal, in certain sculpture and in most landscapes, though not by any means in *all* pictorial art. It is certainly not there in music which, of course, for its part commands the listener's silence.

Many etchers at work in isolation on the isolation of their subject—cathedrals, churches, significant buildings and landmarks—engage this starkness of approach to the limit: no distraction of people, cars, birds, or animals. Meryon, Brangwyn, Cameron, McBey, and Sir Muirhead Bone, for example, would add some action—Bone quite often mechanical and engineering action. Meryon, with his outlandish skaters on the sidewalk, or with the running, gesticulating man brandishing the sword in "La Morgue"; or with those unexpected birds in headlong flight, could bring his work to the brink of madness. But other architectural etchers, such as William Walcot and John Taylor Arms, avoid all distracting elements in order to reach what Sir Hugh Clifford called "The further side of silence." Is it not an act of reverence? For it is clear beyond doubt in Chamberlain the photographer that he surrounds his camera studies of old houses, rooms, churches, buildings, schools, historic landmarks with a stable vacuum. He asks only good weather, lovely cloud effects if available, sunlight and obedient shadows; no people whose clothes and hats (if any) so quickly go out of style; no automobiles (for accent) awaiting patiently their turn to show how out-of-date they are. I can't imagine an artist who loved good food, good wine, good talk, good friendship more than this receptive man. Nor can I imagine, reflecting on what little I know of his totemic life, any other artist of his multiple gifts who concentrated so objectively on whatever work was in progress, honoring not simply (and very deeply) a commemorative silence such as those once called for at sea, but invoking the shelter of a cosmic silence protecting, as it almost seems, his unshakable belief in this our only world.

David McCord

CHRONOLOGY OF THE ARTIST'S LIFE

1895

October 28: Born in Cresco, Iowa, only son and elder child of Dr. George Ellsworth Chamberlain and Cora Lee (Summers) Chamberlain.

1901

Chamberlains moved to frontier lumbering town of Aberdeen, Washington. Mrs. Chamberlain, trained as an elementary school teacher, greatly supplemented son's schooling.

1913

September: Entered University of Washington in Seattle. Studied architecture under Professor Carl Gould, Harvard graduate.

1915

September: Enrolled as sophomore in School of Architecture of Massachusetts Institute of Technology in Boston. At this time, Ralph Adams Cram headed School of Architecture.

1917

June: Following junior year at Massachusetts Institute of Technology, embarked for France as volunteer in American Field Service, Section 14. The first of Chamberlain's many journeys to France. Drove ambulances on Western Front for French infantry divisions.

1918

Transferred to American Army for remainder of tour of duty.

1919

April: Returned to United States, arriving at Newport News, Virginia, and traveled to Fort Lewis, Washington, for discharge from Army. Stayed six months with parents in Aberdeen, Washington.

Autumn: Returned to Boston and lived at 9 Walnut Street on Beacon Hill. Resumed architectural studies at Massachusetts Institute of Technology, where William Emerson had become Dean of School of Architecture. Formed instant friendship, founded on common love for France. Friendship expanded and deepened as William Emerson became his respected teacher, beloved friend, and one of the greatest influences in the artist's life.

1920

February: Discontinued studies at Massachusetts Institute of Technology and worked in Boston as commercial artist and as renderer for architectural firms.

1921

Autumn: Moved to Seattle, Washington, and continued to work in commercial art.

1922

April: Abandoned life as commercial artist, converted remaining resources to ready cash, and departed for France.

Summer: Traveled in France, some of the time with William Emerson. Produced many sketches that later appeared in books and other publications.

September: On return voyage to the United States, met Narcissa Gellatly, who had served with the American Committee for Devastated France and was returning home.

Settled in New York City, making and selling sketches and drawings to architectural magazines. Became engaged to Miss Gellatly.

1923

Early spring: Received American Field Service Scholarship.

April 27: Married Narcissa Gellatly in Grace Church, New York City. The following day, with bride, sailed for France.

Late spring and summer: Traveled and sketched in northern France.

October: Traveled by train in the Iberian Peninsula making sketches and drawings in Burgos, Segovia, Madrid, Seville, and Córdoba. Voyaged from Gibraltar to North Africa, visiting Constantine, Algiers, and Tunis. Took steamer to Palermo, Sicily, and spent Christmas in Taormina.

1924

February: Continued travel to Salerno, Naples, Amalfi, and Florence.

Early spring: Returned by way of Provence to Paris, lived at the Hôtel Jacob et d'Angleterre in rue Jacob, and studied lithography with Gaston Dorfinant in atelier on Île-de-la-Cité, Paris.

Late spring: Traveled in Spain, completing drawings for portfolio *Sketches of Northern Spanish Architecture*, while his wife and her mother sojourned in France. Returned to France shortly before his wife's confinement.

June 17: Birth of first child, a daughter, Narcisse, at the American Hospital, Neuilly-sur-Seine.

Autumn, winter: Studied etching, soft-ground etching, aquatint, and drypoint with Monsieur Edouard Léon in atelier at 6 rue Vercingetorix, Paris.

1925

First etching published, print No. 1, *A Side Street in Beauvais*, and first drypoint published, print No. 23, *The Bridge of Pinos, Spain*.

Summer: Sailed with wife and daughter Narcisse to United States. Visited wife's parents in Westport, Connecticut, then his parents in Aberdeen, Washington.

September: Took assistant professorship in the School of Architecture, University of Michigan, Ann Arbor, Michigan. Taught second-year design, freehand drawing, and outdoor sketching.

1926

June: Sailed for France with wife and daughter. Summered in Normandy, staying at Arromanches—known in World War II as Port Winston—and Bizy-Vernon, with sketching trips to Pont Audemer, Vitré, Josselin, and Dinan. Accompanied part of time by friend, Alexander Calder. Toured Anjou, Touraine, and Burgundy. Traveled south to Antibes and wintered on Riviera at Villefranche-sur-Mer and Menton. Completed work for portfolio *Domestic Architecture in Rural France*.

1927

Spring: Received notice of award of fellowship from John Simon Guggenheim Memorial Foundation for further study of print media.

Autumn: Settled wife and child in Paris apartment on rue Schoelcher near Montparnasse, found lodging for himself in London, enrolled in Royal College of Art, and studied drypoint with Sir Malcolm Osborne, R.A.

1928

April: Completed study in London, returned to Paris, and supervised printing of recently engraved etchings and drypoints.

May: Returned to England, accompanied by wife and architectural student, Louis Skidmore, to research material for book, *Tudor Homes of England*. Skidmore supplied measured drawings. Summered at Étretat in Normandy.

Autumn: Sailed with family for United States to visit the Gellatlys in Connecticut. Rented room in Commodore Hotel in New York City and completed work on *Tudor Homes of England*. Traveled to Boston, Cleveland, Detroit, Chicago, and New York for exhibitions of his work, lectures, and demonstrations of etching process.

1929

Winter, spring: Taught classes in draftsmanship and graphic arts at School of Architecture, Massachusetts Institute of Technology. Drove weekly to Cambridge, Massachusetts, from family home in Connecticut.

Spring: Returned to France with wife and daughter.

May: Made "formal debut" in Paris art world with

one-man show at Galerie Simonson. Summered again at Étretat, Normandy. Worked on drypoints, including American subjects; for instance, No. 80, *Oil.*

Autumn: Family moved with household to apartment in Paris on rue de Lisbonne for winter.

1930

Winter: Purchased and remodeled house in Senlis, Oise, where family took up residence in June. Traveled in Burgundy and the Midi making drawings of brickwork for book, *The Use of Brick in French Architecture,* by William Emerson.

Late fall: Took business trip to United States. Returned early in January 1931.

1931

February 18: Birth of second child, a daughter, Stephanie, in American Hospital, Neuilly-sur-Seine. Chamberlain's mother came to stay with family until autumn 1931.

Spring, summer: Continued work on drawings for *The Use of Brick in French Architecture.*

1932

Autumn: Closed Senlis house and sailed with family for United States to recoup financial base. Stayed with Gellatlys in Greenfield Hill, Connecticut, for a year. Set up studio in barn and later in caretaker's house.

1933

Spring: Commuted to New Haven to make sketches of Yale for drypoints subsequently published by Yale University Press as portfolio *Twelve Etchings of Yale* (1933–34). Received commission for series of covers for periodical *Pencil Points.*

June: Returned with family to France. Lived and worked in Senlis for following year.

1934

Late summer: Leased house in Senlis to French army officer. Sailed for United States and stayed again with Gellatlys in Greenfield Hill, Connecticut. Received first photographic commission from Yale University Press, to make photographic postcards to commemorate Connecticut Tercentenary. "American Scene" postcards followed in subsequent years.

Autumn: Took post as lecturer in graphic arts at Massachusetts Institute of Technology. Rented home in Chestnut Hill, Massachusetts, for a year.

Summer: Motored throughout New England, visiting Moffat family in Vinal Haven, Maine, a vacation practice that continued for many of the following fifteen years.

1935

Autumn: Resumed teaching post at Massachusetts Institute of Technology. Rented furnished house in Marblehead, Massachusetts, where family spent winter. Worked on plates of French, English, and American subjects. Printed plates himself at Massachusetts Institute of Technology on fine old French press obtained from architectural department.

1936

Began lifelong association with Walter Frese, founder and President of Hastings House, publisher of Chamberlain's photographic books.

Summer: Toured New England photographing its scenes and architecture, a project Chamberlain engaged in whenever time allowed until a few years before his death.

1937

April: Purchased house at 31 Front Street, Marblehead, remodeled it, and moved in that autumn.

1938

Spring: Sailed to Cannes for prolonged visit with friends, the Alexander Stollers, at Cap Ferrat on French Riviera.

Summer: Completed Williamsburg etchings, printed by Edmond Rigal in Paris studio, under shadow of war scare in Europe.

1939

January: Returned to United States to teach at Massachusetts Institute of Technology during spring semester. Wife and children remained in France.

May: Wife and daughters, accompanied by French maid, sailed on *Rotterdam* for United States.

Summer: Resettled at 31 Front Street, Marblehead. Published first photographically illustrated engagement calendars. Continued publication of them yearly for remainder of his life. Worked on first of gastronomic books, *Clementine in the Kitchen*, published in 1943 after Chamberlain had gone overseas in World War II.

1942

Autumn: Enlisted in Army Air Force. Was commissioned captain and sent to Officers' Training School in Miami Beach, Florida; to photo intelligence school in Harrisburg, Pennsylvania; and to Atlantic City, New Jersey, to await assignment. Spent brief time at Fort Hamilton, New York, awaiting departure overseas.

1943

April: Departed with other American Army officers from New York by small ship of Philippine registry. Arrived seventy-five days later in Cairo, Egypt. Was transferred to Sidi Bou Said, Tunisia.

1944

Late winter: Moved to Italy on military photographic assignment, was stationed at Pomigliano d'Arco, lived in school house.

March: Witnessed eruption of Vesuvius.

Summer and fall: Assigned to San Severo. Completed military photographic assignments from Elba to Romania. Received Legion of Merit for photographic reports on enemy defenses.

1945

February: Flew to London to publish report of strategic bombing survey.

May: Took leave in France to evaluate state of long-neglected house in Senlis.

October: Returned, by plane, to United States, arriving in New York City.

1946

February 15: Relieved of active military duty at Pentagon in Washington, D.C., and returned to Marblehead. Found studio space over Osborne's Grocery Store, Marblehead, and used space for following twenty-one years.

Spring: Made first of many trips to Williamsburg, Virginia, accompanied by wife, to research information and compose book *Behold Williamsburg*.

Autumn: Purchased Bubier Mansion (built c. 1710–

20) on Tucker Street in Marblehead. Lived there, when not traveling, for the remainder of his life.

1947

Visited Mount Vernon, Virginia. Photographed subjects to illustrate revised handbook of George Washington's home.

1949

Spring and summer: Sailed with wife for France. Began methodical "epicurean tour of French provinces." Wrote and illustrated essays that appeared in magazine *Gourmet* and later in book *Bouquet de France*. Traveled to England. Visited Miss Phyllis Dunthorne of Rembrandt Galleries, London, English agent for his published prints. Visited many wartime friends.

Late summer: Completed sale of Senlis house.

Fall and winter: Returned home to Marblehead.

1950

Spring: Sailed to France, again accompanied by wife, and continued previous year's epicurean travels in French provinces.

Summer: Collected material for articles, books, and French calendars.

Autumn: Returned home to United States for winter.

1951

Spring: Sailed for France with wife, on third and final research trip for *Bouquet de France*.

Autumn: Returned to United States and spent most of following year in Marblehead writing and designing *Bouquet de France*.

1953

Winter: Visited Charleston, South Carolina. Photographed houses and researched information for book *Southern Interiors*.

Spring: Motored through New England gathering photographs for book and calendar illustrations.

Fall: Returned to Europe with wife and daughter Stephanie. Traveled in southern France and northern Italy photographing, sketching, and taking notes for proposed book, *Italian Bouquet*, companion volume of *Bouquet de France*.

1954

Spring: Returned to Marblehead.

1955

Summer: Made second trip with wife to Italy to research material for *Italian Bouquet*.

1956

Summer, fall, and winter: Made third and final trip to Italy for information for *Italian Bouquet*.

1957

Spring: Returned to Marblehead.

1958

Wrote and designed *Italian Bouquet*.

1959

Summer: Traveled in England with wife. Photographed, sketched, and researched material for book *British Bouquet*. Trip was first of four through British Isles during four consecutive summers. Wife accompanied him on first three trips.

1962

Fall and winter: Remained in Marblehead; compiled, wrote, and designed *British Bouquet*.

1963

Summer: Traveled to France to research material for new edition of *Bouquet de France*. Made two additional trips to France in summers of 1964 and 1965. Completed research for new volume that, by his own account, was most ambitious book to date.

1965

Spring: Sailed on Swedish cruise ship *Kungsholm* with wife for "Spring Garden Cruise" to Azores, Spain, Ireland, Great Britain, and Holland. Wrote photographically illustrated travel article on trip for magazine *Gourmet*. Included recipes gathered by his wife.

1966

Summer: Moved studio from loft over Osborne's Grocery Store to more convenient first-story space where, except for period of illness, continued to work for remainder of his life.

Autumn: Sailed from New York on *Gripsholm*. Visited Tangiers, Gibralta, Malta, Taormina, and other Mediterranean ports, as well as Lisbon, the coast of Spain, and Scandinavian countries. Took photographs for the cruise line to use in promotional brochures. Visited Egmont Peterson, of Peterson Printing Company in Copenhagen, Denmark, where several of Chamberlain's books had been printed, including latest edition of *Bouquet de France*.

1967

Worked on autobiography, published under the title *Etched in Sunlight* by the Boston Public Library in 1968. During following period, Boston Public Library purchased comprehensive collection of Chamberlain's graphic works, including photographic enlargements.

1970

February: Flew to Jamaica with wife for few weeks' vacation at Ocho Rios.

Spring and summer: Traveled in northeastern United States photographing interiors of historic houses in Maine, New Hampshire, and Massachusetts for inclusion in book, *New England Rooms (1639–1863)*, written in collaboration with wife.

September: Sailed with wife for France on the *Queen Elizabeth II* for visit with friends at Chateau of Chaudenay and holiday in Burgundy. Trip was Samuel Chamberlain's last to Europe.

1971

Spring: Traveled in Rhode Island and Connecticut. Photographed interiors and researched material for *New England Rooms (1639–1863)*.

1972

October: Honored at party at Ritz Carlton Hotel in Boston, given by publisher, Walter Frese, to celebrate publication of *New England Rooms (1639–1863)*, last book published in his lifetime. A few days later, hospitalized in Salem, Massachusetts.

1973

February: Returned home after nearly four months in hospital to recuperate from surgery.

April: Celebrated fiftieth wedding anniversary at home with close friends.

1974

Worked on revision of book *Old Marblehead* for bicentennial edition, completed and published after his death by wife.

1975

January 10: After short illness, died in Mary Alley Hospital, Marblehead.

1975

September, October: Exhibition, *Samuel Chamberlain, A Memorial Exhibition of his Drawings and Prints*, organized by June and Norman Kraeft under the sponsorship of American Institute of Architects Foundation and Boston Public Library, with works selected from Wiggin Collection at Library and Kraefts' private collection. Exhibited at The Octagon, Washington, D.C., headquarters of the American Institute of Architects Foundation.

1976

July: Memorial exhibition, *Samuel Chamberlain Review*, displayed drypoints, lithographs, pencil drawings, watercolor, books, Wedgwood plates, and artist's decorations and medals. Organized by Marblehead Arts Association and shown at "King" Hooper Mansion, Marblehead.

1977

November, December: Exhibition at Birmingham Museum of Art, Birmingham, Alabama, *Works by Samuel Chamberlain*, contained same drawings and prints as earlier show at The Octagon, as well as photographs from collection of Ed Willis Barnett of Birmingham. Exhibition was joint effort of Ed Willis Barnett and Sinclair H. Hitchings, of Cambridge, Massachusetts.

1978

March, April: *Samuel Chamberlain, Photographer*, exhibition of original photographic prints organized by Sinclair H. Hitchings, Keeper of Prints at Boston Public Library, exhibited in Wiggin Gallery of Library.

1981

April: Exhibition, *Three M.I.T. Etchers*, at Margaret Hutchinson Compton Gallery, Massachusetts Institute of Technology, Cambridge, was organized by Warren Seamans of Massachusetts Institute of Technology Museum. Exhibited were prints by John Taylor Arms, Samuel Chamberlain, and Louis C. Rosenberg, loaned by June and Norman Kraeft of June 1 Gallery, Bethlehem, Connecticut.

July: Exhibition of fifteen prints selected from the collection of the artist's widow. Exhibit was conceived and organized by Lease A. Plimpton of Massachusetts Institute of Technology, Lincoln Laboratories, Lexington, Massachusetts.

ESSAYS

WHEN a friend of Samuel Chamberlain was asked recently to give a brief talk in his memory, he referred to Sam's own comments in his autobiography, *Etched in Sunlight*, about the two world wars in which he took active part as a volunteer. He did not speak of campaigns, of battles, of the grim and ugly things he had seen. His cherished memory of World War I was of helping to pick the grapes in the Champagne in the autumn sunlight of 1917. The *vendange* was accomplished, an old ritual of the good life survived for yet another year. In World War II, he never lost an opportunity to explore old bookshops to pick up an eighteenth-century volume on gastronomy or examples of beautiful typography or book design. In his photographs of enemy defenses, taken in the course of his duties as an intelligence officer in Italy, he managed somehow to include here and there a flock of sheep on a road or the picturesque silhouettes of black-robed priests walking along a ruined street, stubbornly making these utilitarian records of ugly subject matter into compositions designed by an artist.

With this, it must be remembered that he fought his way with determination and voluntarily into service in both world wars because of a strong sense of duty and moral obligation. But when it was all over, what he distilled from the dislocations of war was human compassion, his lasting love of the good things in life, and his perceptions of beauty, which he never failed to find in almost any circumstance.

It is not easy to be objective about a life which has been so closely involved with one's own through over half a century—or to assess a character so complicated and yet so simple as Sam Chamberlain's. Two things are very clear: his love of beauty and his extraordinary capacity for hard work; his productivity was enormous, his versatility and variety of talents were truly prodigious. And yet, with all of that, it was his human qualities that were memorable—a unique sense of humor, generosity, and a certain simplicity that remained unspoiled by success and recognition. He was still sometimes the wide-eyed boy from the West Coast with the hard-work ethic of that background, and sophistication never really changed him. Perhaps this is the true measure of humility.

NARCISSA GELLATLY CHAMBERLAIN

FEW ARTISTS have given as lucid, genial, and complete an account of themselves as Samuel Chamberlain. His autobiography, *Etched in Sunlight*, published by the Boston Public Library in 1968, was designed by him and illustrated by a profusion of those of his prints and photographs that he liked best; that is the permanent and definitive work to which all must refer. In this brief tribute I can only note his contributions to architectural history as a printmaker and photographer.

Samuel Chamberlain left the Massachusetts Institute of Technology School of Architecture during World War I to join the American Field Service. Having lost his heart to France, he stayed for as many years as he could manage, drawing architectural subjects. In 1924 he published a portfolio of *Vingt Lithographies du Vieux Paris*, but soon turned to etching, and then to drypoint, which became his favorite medium. As this was a period when architects still sought inspiration from the work of their predecessors, he did during the next five years for the Architectural Book Publishing Co., Inc., of New York three books that were admirable additions to any architect's library: *Sketches of Northern Spanish Architecture* (1925), *Domestic Architecture in Rural France* (1928), and *Tudor Homes of England* (1929). In 1935 there appeared the first of a projected series of his pencil drawings entitled *The Use of Brick in French Architecture*. As "the depression had an intensifying effect on expatriate American artists," Chamberlain produced a portfolio of twelve etchings of Yale, well publicized by the Yale University Press. Before long it seemed prudent to return to the United States, where the Massachusetts Institute of Technology offered him a post as lecturer in the graphic arts. So the Chamberlain family moved from Senlis to Marblehead.

Having returned to the United States, Samuel Chamberlain not only chose local subjects for his prints, but added photography with a Zeiss Orix camera and later a 5 x 7 Linhof camera to his techniques. Although by 1950 he had become primarily a photographer and writer, he was not of the snap-snap-snap school that takes a score of shots on the chance that one will be good. He exercised as meticulous care in making a photograph as in a drypoint. Having planned his composition in advance, he did not take a picture if the weather refused to furnish the light and shade that he required. I recall a day at the Hancock Shaker Community when he had his camera on a tripod for hours but never opened the shutter, for the sun proved disobliging. But when he was satisfied, the result would have gladdened the heart of the long-dead architect whose work he had so subtly recorded.

In 1936 he began publishing books of photographic studies of American buildings, towns, and landscapes, eventually producing more than fifty volumes, that, through their wide distribution, have had great influence in making the American people aware of the beauty and significance of historic buildings. His books on Charleston, Williamsburg, Boston, and Salem gave many Americans their first taste for the architecture of the past. I wish Henry Adams might have seen the photographic illustrations that Samuel Chamberlain did for the Limited Editions Club printing of *Mont-Saint-Michel and Chartres* in 1957. They are the perfect accompaniment for the text, but each is a work of art in itself.

Although Samuel Chamberlain, once he left for World War I, never returned to the formal study and practice of architecture, he became one of its great interpreters. It was appropriate for the American Institute of Architects to elect him to honorary membership, and fitting that the Institute organized a memorial exhibition of his work.

WALTER MUIR WHITEHILL

SAMUEL CHAMBERLAIN'S gentle wit and sense of fun were disarming. Was this easygoing man the draftsman, etcher, photographer, and author of many books? His work was often alone, his relaxation in company, but his legion of friends learned from his pictures and prose what quiet vision he possessed. He planned and carried out a staggering number of enterprises. A natural man, he found himself early, and enjoyed fifty productive years. Letters written while he commanded a well-deserved share of the "etching boom" of the twenties are not a whit different in their tone and their relish of life from his speech and his writing half a century later, when to "etcher" many other occupations had been added. As formal titles, his occupations would make an impressive recital. All were devoted to the enhancement of life. Among them should be emblazoned the title of traveler, for he stands in the ranks of those who made a vocation of travel and an art of describing it. On his journeys he carried with him his sense of craftsmanship, and for this, too, he deserves to be remembered. He cultivated the disciplines of hand and eye and practised them with thought, care, and skill.

The present volume takes its departure from his love of architecture and early passion for pencil drawing and finds its theme in the extension of this absorbing pleasure and interest into printmaking media, above all, the sharp cutting medium of drypoint.

A close look at his printmaking begins with his lithographic studies of Paris in 1924, is soon dominated by the great plates of European cathedrals, but gradually yields a sense of his discovery of beauty in many different moments and places. For him a glimpse of a roadside junk shop could yield a subject, and he could venture successfully into landscape to capture the hot stillness of midday and midsummer along a dusty French road. The crash of '29 and the decline of a market for prints deprived us of a series of drypoints that in subject provide counterpoint to his European studies. He began his prints of contemporary American cities and American industry in 1929, and made only a few.

For all who read these lines, a return to Chamberlain's books is recommended. Through them his prose and photographs can be enjoyed, and some of them include drawings and prints as well. The diligent reader will find excellent recipes and a great deal of pleasurable armchair travel along the way. So prolific a maker of books becomes, almost by definition, a maker of taste, and Chamberlain's influence remains a benevolent one. It is impossible to mourn such a man, for in his abiding love of life he is with us, sharing as well as enlarging our own experience.

SINCLAIR H. HITCHINGS

THIS SALUTE to Samuel Chamberlain would hardly be complete without a note on his writings. He put words together with much the same grace, probity, and warmth that characterize his etchings. He wrote not only of architecture and cuisine but also of fellow artists. In his autobiography he tells of the day when the noted portrait etcher Arthur Heintzelman, newly returned from France, moved to Marblehead, Massachusetts, and the Chamberlains and Heintzelmans found themselves neighbors. He continues:

By the following June (of 1940), for a day at least, Marblehead became the print center of America. To honor Frank W. Benson, the dean of American etchers who lived in nearby Salem, the local arts association arranged a retrospective exhibition of ninety Benson prints, mostly of his famous wild fowl. . . .

Five graphic artists gathered in the old King Hooper Mansion, the home of a prosperous merchant shipper in Colonial days, and demonstrated the art of the copperplate medium to an audience that poured into Marblehead from Boston and the North Shore. John Taylor Arms brought his etching press from Greenfield Hill and demonstrated the art of pure etching as only he could do it. He cleaned the plate, waxed it, smoked it and needled it with both hands, never stopping his stentorian monologue for an instant. While his enthralled audience watched breathlessly, he protected the plate with stopping out varnish, bit it in several immersions of acid, cleaned it, and triumphantly printed a proof before his time had run out. At the conclusion his listeners were limp with exhaustion, but he was as fresh as ever.

. . . Each of the other print makers occupied an old paneled room in the mansion and showed his specialty. Arthur Heintzelman made a drypoint of a round-faced little boy who sat patiently in a chair. Thomas Nason, the gifted engraver from Connecticut, executed a delicate copper engraving, and I made a soft ground etching of the King Hooper Mansion itself. For a plate printer, we had the very best, none other than Kerr Eby, whose dramatic etchings of World War I had made him famous. He pulled prints from all four demonstration plates under the friendly gaze of Frank Benson and the popping flashlights of Boston news photographers. . . .

A search of the archives of writings on twentieth-century American printmaking turned up articles by Chamberlain on the work of two of his printmaking friends, Arms and Benson. Here is an excerpt from "John Taylor Arms . . . Phenomenon" in the March, 1941, issue of *Print, A Quarterly Journal of the Graphic Arts*:

Decidedly, John Arms is an exception among etchers. No other American printmaker has reached so wide an audience. None knows so many of his fellow etchers by their first names. No five of them have put so much devoted labor into the Cause of Etching. He belongs to a bewildering list of print societies. Anything which brings art to the common man, particularly the etcher's art, has his immediate support. . . . Any young etcher about to embark on his career has a firm potential friend in him. He serves on endless committees and juries, arranges countless exhibitions and writes more letters than a Congressman up for reelection. And in the meantime he manages to execute the most minutely-etched plates ever attempted in American printmaking. . . .

This zeal for searching out the last iota of detail and texture results in such immaculately-finished plates that some people find his ecclesiastical etchings cold at first sight. Reading only an intellectual quality in them, they expect to find the etcher a cold and aloof perfectionist. They are due for a surprise when they meet John Arms, for they will be struck first of all by his personal warmth and friendliness. The ardor and energy of this man are coupled with another quality—an immense kindliness. The spiritual quality which underlies his etchings springs from the affection which he feels for his fellow man as well as for his own work. . . .

And, in an article, "Frank W. Benson—The Etcher," in *The Print Collector's Quarterly* for April, 1938, Chamberlain tells of the response of visitors to the first exhibition ever held of Frank Benson's etchings (Boston, 1915):

Their reaction to etchings of ducks in flight was not merely favorable, it was electric. Quite by accident a new, crystal-clear note in etching had been rung. Another brilliant epigram had been added to the vocabulary of the copper plate. . . .

His were not static birds. They abounded with motion and vitality. There was freedom in their flight, and freedom in the approach of the artist who had stumbled upon the innovation of etching them. For here a painter was etching, unfettered by too much minutiae, too crushing a knowledge of the complexity of his medium. A consummate draftsman before he took up etching, a lover of birds from childhood, he possessed that inestimably rare quality of patience, combined with restless curiosity, which enabled him to strive constantly to solve the baffling problem of the bitten line, the refinements and tribulations of drypoint. Benson was a tireless experimentor, spurred on by a divine discontent with his work, and aspiring some day to do an etching which entirely pleased him. A restless explorer he still is, etching in a sky and spending hours taking it out. Scraping, burnishing and polishing, he often puts a plate through half a dozen different states in search of the fine balance of black and white which marks his great plates.

The words of praise Samuel Chamberlain bestowed on his fellow New England etchers apply in full measure to the etcher who wrote them. A further glimpse of the etcher as writer shows his dedication to the unique qualities of etching as a means of expression. In "The Triumphal Arches of Piranesi" in *The Print Collector's Quarterly* for February, 1937, he goes back two hundred years to describe and analyze the first important set of Piranesi etchings. He writes:

In 1748, the young engraver published a set of smaller etchings, calling them *Antichita Romane de' Tempi della Republica*. This group reveals an entirely new view of his work, and permits a more adequate appreciation of his unquestioned mastery in pure etching. This is not the grandiloquent Piranesi, but a modest young man, enamored of his subject and superbly equipped to record it with the bitten line. This is a subtler Piranesi, dependant not upon dramatization and overwhelming dimensions, but upon deft needling, simple biting and an enchanting balance of black and white.

It is tempting to quote at greater length, but perhaps appropriate to end with these words reflecting Chamberlain's own values.

Juⁿe and Norman Kraeft

PRINTMAKING ACCORDING TO CHAMBERLAIN

THREE ESSAYS by SAMUEL CHAMBERLAIN

Etching as a Medium of Architectural Expression

OPINIONS vary, but many are the critics who believe that an etching is the finest and the ultimate setting on paper for a worthy piece of architecture. There is something about the atmospheric vibrancy of an etching which imparts a peculiar and irresistible life to architectural drawing, something in an acid bitten copper furrow which often has a greater expressiveness than mere pen or pencil lines. There is the association of fine old Japanese papers, of skilled printing by some tottering old craftsman, and a certain permanency which an etching always suggests. An etching, due to its veiled inking, may hold together where a pencil sketch will not. A copper plate offers receptive ground to the meticulous detailed drawing which so often appeals to the architect. In fact, there are dozens of reasons why architects have turned into etchers—and etchers have turned to architecture as a source of inspiration.

Without question it is a medium with a peculiar charm for the architect. To compile a list of those architects who have dabbled in it and finally succumbed to its appeal and forsaken their profession would entail a formidable amount of research. But the number would be enlightening, particularly among the English etchers of the last hundred years.

Of the more recent etchers who have thus strayed from the T-square, perhaps William Walcot is the most conspicuous example. Walcot is admirable in that he is proud of his architectural past and gives one no opportunity to ignore it in his etchings. The handling is always that of an exquisite architectural draftsman, grown into a master etcher. His plates, particularly those of his restorations, are unforgettable to any lover of draftsmanship. John Taylor Arms, Louis Rosenberg and Alonzo Webb, all architects at one time, seem permanently won over to copper plates. Many Frenchmen in the Ecole des Beaux-Arts play dual roles of architects and etchers without apparent handicap. Monsieur Carlu, at present a professor of design in this country, has brought forth some magnificent plates.

Hedley Fitton, in many ways, seems to give the happiest expression of all to architectural form, clothing it in soft, yet positive values. His perspective is masterful in its perfection.

A master such as Brangwyn is interested more in the dramatic force of his subject than in its architectural detail. This is one of the reasons why architects in America hold such varied opinions of his work. A man to man canvass among them reveals that many are boundlessly enthusiastic about his etchings, while others are left impressed but unsympathetic. There is no middle neutral ground in judging work as forceful as Brangwyn's.

There is a clique of American etchers, quite resigned and attached to the Latin Quarter, who seemingly refuse to leave Paris. Almost all of them, save one, lean toward architectural subjects. Prominent among them is Louis Orr, whose etchings of the Cathedral of Rheims formed such a prominent part of the baggage of returning American officers after the war. Orr possesses a vast knowledge of the technical possibilities of his medium and his plates are as finished as some of the meticulous old engravings of a couple of centuries ago. What he is able to record as documentary evidence is little short of astounding. One is tempted to compare his work with that of Haig or Piranesi.

Alonzo Webb, an architect who has either found himself or gone astray, according to the point of view, brought an architect's sketching equipment in contact with copper plates, acid and needles, with interesting results. A retrospective study of his plates reveals how intelligent and successful has been his "loosening-up" process. Robert Logan, who etches architecture almost exclusively, recently visited this country and produced two large plates of the Harkness Memorial towers in New Haven. Arthur William Heintzelman, at present the most acclaimed of the little colony, is more of a figure artist. He has received more medals and awards than an international billiard star. There remain the Armingtons, John V. Winkler and several others whose work is better known in France than in their native land.

It is entirely logical that an architect should use etching as a medium for some of his renderings, but whether the question is possessed of much practicability I am not able to state. The step from pencil and pen to an etching needle is more natural and considerably easier than an architect ordinarily thinks. A certain mental readjustment (for, of course, the drawing must be done in reverse), and a bit of technical experimentation are needed, true enough. The one considerable obstruction which stands in the way is this mechanical complexity which, unfortunately, is not conquered on first trial, or on the second.

The etchings here reproduced may be of interest as the maiden attempts of a hand principally accustomed to pencil. It is true that a certain directness, freshness and spontaneity which characterize pencil presentation are apt to be lost at first in the indirect medium of etching, as these immature attempts probably reveal.

One unforgettable advantage which an etching possesses as an architectural rendering is that any number of prints can be made; also that the plate can be corrected and retouched repeatedly, and that the very fact that the subject is reproduced in copper makes an effective impression.

Soft ground etching is a sympathetic medium to one accustomed to pencil drawing. It is difficult at first to lay a good soft ground, but the great advantage is that the etching is done with a pencil and a bit of tracing paper laid over the ground, rather than with unfamiliar needles and burins. The result is rather surprising—the softness of a pencil line is reproduced in copper. The etching of "Old Houses in Lisieux" was done in this way. Nothing but a lead pencil and acid was used in etching the plate. Drypoint has another unique advantage. It needs no acid bath, of course, doing away with the tinkerings of an amateur chemist in the family sink, and is, so far as I know, the only sketching medium unimpeded and unhurt by rainfall. The "Springtime in Senlis" plate was done entirely in a dismal downpour.

Of course, the question arises: who would be dumb enough to try to draw in the rain?

—*American Architect*, Vol. CXXVIII, No. 2478, pp. 119–122, August 12, 1925.

Lithographic Processes in Architectural Illustration

SHEER DRAFTSMANSHIP probably has a better expression in lithography than in any other reproductive medium. To verify this, it is only necessary to regard the work of the English lithographers who flourished in the middle of the last century. What a magnificent clique of draftsmen they were! Everyone has his favorite among them. Boys is my particular hero; I could feast on his enchanted plates from now till doomsday. But they were almost equal in their genius for architectural expression. A glance at the work of Boys or of Prout is more eloquent of the splendid architectural possibilities of lithography than many pages of these pale paragraphs which follow.

It is a medium peculiarly fitted to the architect. Very little experience is required of him before he obtains most encouraging results. Some crayons, a stone or a sheet of transfer paper, a razor blade and there you are, ready to begin. The anguish of the mechanical side is left to the printer. A lithographic crayon can be subjected to practically all of the manipulations of a lead pencil. The harder crayons can be sharpened to give a fine, wiry line; the softer ones can produce a juicy blackness not even found in charcoal.

Perfectly good pen and inks can be put on the stone, either as strong in blacks as a wood cut or as delicate as a competition sketch for a small house. Incidentally, those who are interested in the advance of draftsmanship in this country must derive a vast pleasure from the beautiful pen and ink renderings which pour into the competitions held by the building material organizations. Mastery of this medium is not confined to the English alone.

The finest quality of lithographic impression is undoubtedly obtained by drawing directly on the smooth, creamy surface of the stone. In no other way can the full richness, the wide possibilities of lithography be fully utilized. In this respect, few artists have obtained as much from stone as Bolton Brown, long a member of the Woodstock art colony. Mr. Brown, so I am told, has solved the mysteries of lithography unaided, after years of experiment. He has perfected his own method of treating the stone, his own way of printing, and even makes his own crayons. Some of the grains that he obtains are so soft and delicate and beautifully modelled that they make most of the contemporaneous European lithographs look as coarse as circus posters in comparison. He gives an expressiveness to foliage such as few of the old masters of the medium have excelled. Many are those who had come to consider such modelling as almost a lost art. I am informed that the late George Bellows, surely as fine a lithographer as we can boast, was completely won over to Mr. Brown's methods. As a consequence, the astonishing strength and daring and skill apparent in a Bellows lithograph are hardly secondary to the superb quality of the print. One feels that not a particle of the artist's forceful draftsmanship has been weakened. Lithography was surely the medium for the cavernous blacks and the brilliant contrasts of which Bellows was so fond.

Working on stone entails the necessity of drawing backwards of course, and makes it inconvenient to work outside of the studio. For those who prefer outdoor sketching it is obviously a far simpler affair to draw on transfer paper. In the first place, one is not required to draw in reverse, doing away with much mental calisthenics and confusion, as well as the mirror on the open air easel, into which some artists are prone to peer intently like crystal gazers. Also if working on location, as say the movie directors, one becomes impressed with the fact that a sheet of transfer paper is somewhat more transportable than a two-hundred pound stone. Courageous lithographers there are, including the above mentioned Mr. Brown, who strike forth for the morning's work with a well laden wheelbarrow, a grim look and a box of lunch, but to duplicate this zeal in a metropolitan district is really asking too much. A street-corner sketcher gets gaped at as much as a bearded lady as it is.

There are several types of transfer paper, each giving a slightly different quality of line when put on the stone. Many prefer the Japanese paper, but there is a new Hungarian stock which admirably takes the crayon in almost the identical manner of stone. It is difficult for anyone outside the lithographer's family circle to distinguish between a print which originates on this Hungarian stock and one which comes from a drawing made directly on the stone.

Any number of fine papers are suitable for lithographic prints. They can be more fragile, more varied in texture than the papers used in printing etchings. A glueless Japan rice paper makes a splendid proof, as does a sheet of gossamer thinness. Old Italian and French papers, provided they are free from too much glue, make exquisite prints. Colored inks are sometimes used, a sepia being often more sympathetic to certain subjects than black.

The real physical energy in all this business is expended by the printer when he goes about the strenuous business of transferring the drawing to the stone and later laboriously pulling the proofs. The first process calls for no little skill and patience, as well as the application of acid, talcum powder, resin, gum arabic, buckets of water and endless elbow grease. At least, this is the way the Frenchmen do it. The Paris printers are, as far as I know them, quaint, lovable old characters, contentedly puttering about with antiquated sliding pressure presses of exactly the same type that once worked for Daumier and Gavarni. They are vastly in love with their "metier" and always hovering on the brink of bankruptcy due to the unstable financial habits of their artist clients. Photo-engraving has all but wiped out the considerable role that the lithographers used to play in Paris, and the few of the old school that still hold on do so mainly from love of their trade. There are commercial lithographers in all parts of the United States who would find the transferring and printing of a straight lithograph to be a relatively simple task, and in the largest cities there are printers capable of doing very fine work indeed.

I know of no way to gauge the ripple of enthusiasm for lithography which is said to be sweeping the country, but it assuredly seems to have more of a hold now than it did a few years ago. Several of our best known renderers have taken it up seriously with excellent results. Albert Sterner, Joseph Pennell and several others demonstrated its possibilities in posters during the war, as Brangwyn and his associates did in England. Newspaper artists have discovered that a lithographic sketch reproduces well in newsprint; poster artists have made use of its effectiveness. Lithography offers even greater inducements to the architect. Where publicity for a building project is a desirable asset, the value of a forceful lithograph, printed in quantity and wisely displayed, is difficult to estimate. If our interest in drawing keeps pace with our architectural achievements, lithography should find a very definite niche in the affections of American architects. Perhaps a revival is on the way. Perhaps we will uncover work which rivals that of the fine old Englishmen of the eighteen fifties. You never know what may happen in this age.

— *American Architect*, Vol. cxxviii, No. 2480, pp. 207–210, September 9, 1925.

How to Make a Drypoint

THERE IS no *one* way to engrave a drypoint, any more than there is a solitary method, for example, of laying out a perspective or, for that matter, carving a goose. The personal techniques of the etcher, the draftsman or the man who wields the carving knife, enter very prominently into the process. The following brief description deals therefore with but one method, among many, of making a drypoint and no suggestion is made that it is preferable to any other procedure.

A drypoint may be either engraved directly on the copper plate from nature, or it can be worked up in the studio from sketches. The former method is often preferable in the case of a simple landscape. But when portraits or architectural subjects are being considered, a perplexing difficulty crops up. Like the plate of your wedding invitation, which is possibly now converted into a tray for calling cards in your front hall, a drypoint plate must be drawn in reverse to produce a proof which shows the subject in its true sense. To draw directly in reverse requires a prodigious mental effort, especially when the subject is complicated. This usually has an upsetting effect upon the etcher. He finds himself signing his name backwards, eating his breakfast in the evening and adopting a warped view of life in general. Joseph Pennell sometimes neglected to reverse his plates. One of his favorite subjects was the skyline of lower Manhattan seen from his apartment in Brooklyn. Believe it or not, there are plenty of trusting souls who have figured it out that Pennell lived in Jersey!

With architectural subjects, greater accuracy and more studied effect (not that these are necessarily virtues) can be obtained by working in the studio from careful drawings. The task of transferring the drawing to the plate, in reverse, is something of a bore. The principal lines of the subject are traced with a drypoint needle upon a sheet of gelatine paper. Red poncif powder is rubbed into these lines. The copper plate is then waxed and smoked, so that its surface is a dull black. The engraved gelatine paper is placed face down on the smoked plate, and the two are passed through an etching press. This leaves the principal lines of the drawing readily visible in red against the black surface. These are retraced with a ruby point, which cuts the copper very lightly. Once the lines are entirely retraced, the wax is removed with gasoline and there, at last, is your drawing, outlined in reverse. There are less tedious ways of transferring drawings, but I, for one, have found none so accurate. The original drawing is studied in reverse by the simple expedient of turning it upside down and viewing it in a mirror.

It is now about time for the actual cutting of the plate. Either a steel or a diamond point may be used. The diamond point cuts the copper readily in any direction, but only with difficulty can one obtain depth with it. Also diamond points split with surprising ease. The steel point needs constant resharpening, and is a balky instrument at first, but it produces the fresh rich lines and the velvety tones which are so characteristic of drypoint. Most etchers agree that the most difficult phase of drypoint etching lies in keeping the needle really sharp. Half the battle is won if this is mastered. The cutting is done directly on the copper. Wherever the point ploughs into the metal, a ridge is invariably thrown up on one or both sides of the line. When the pasty etching ink is applied, it clings to these burrs of copper causing the juicy, slightly blurred lines which are typical of drypoint.

Visibility is poor on a copper plate. To aid the struggling vision, one can rub a black paste into the lines as they are engraved. This paste is a simple mixture of vaseline and lampblack, and cannot harm the plate. Further aid can be found by working under a screen of white tracing paper or muslin, which is suspended at an angle before a window. The white surface is thus reflected on the copper, greatly aiding the eyes. Ordinary ceiling reflexions usually are not sufficient.

One may stop the engraving of a drypoint at any stage or state, to pull a proof of the work already accomplished. This privilege, not so readily obtained from an etching or aquatint, must not be abused, for drypoint lines on copper are quickly weakened by the wiping of the plate and the flattening action of the press.

Electrolysis comes to the rescue, once a drypoint is finished, and coats the copper plate with an infinitesimal facing of steel. Thus fortified, the plate can stand a hundred proofs or more without apparent weakening, whereas an unfaced copper drypoint will usually become weak and lifeless before a dozen impressions are taken. Zinc plates are even less resistant. Proofs of states of drypoints are consequently few in number, as a rule.

Corrections can be made on the plate as long as any copper remains. Lines which are too strong can be lightened immediately with a triangular scraping instrument or a smooth rounded burnisher. Nor is it difficult to strengthen lines and tones, but the task of completely removing mistakes from the smooth surface of the copper is a veritable calvary of toil and patience.

The printing of a drypoint is another problem. As a rule it does not yield a good impression as readily as an etching plate. To obtain a rich print and yet lose none of the integrity of the lines is the difficulty which worries many a printer. Some solve the matter by barely heating the plate when inking, and by using a terrific pressure on the press.

But such weighty considerations need not concern an enthusiastic beginner. A sketch on copper is not much more difficult than one on paper, to be quite truthful. Anyone in search of mild adventure on the next sketching trip might do well to slip a couple of copper plates in with the conventional pads and pencils. There lies ahead that quite unforgettable moment when the first proof of one's first drypoint is pulled from the press. That is worth a lot. Besides, it is about time America produced another Whistler.

—*American Architect*, Vol. CXXXX, No. 2600, pp. 22–25, 80, October 1931.

A GUIDE TO THE PRINTS

THIS VOLUME represents the authors' mutually dedicated efforts to research and organize information about Samuel Chamberlain's works in drypoint, etching, and lithography. The resulting catalogue raisonné classifies each of two hundred and eighty-six prints executed by the artist between 1924 and 1975, the year of his death. Although Chamberlain himself tended to catalogue only those prints, one hundred and forty-three in all, that he planned to publish and offer for sale through his dealers, nearly all of his works in graphic media have been reproduced in publications at one time or another during the past fifty years. Consequently, discovery of prints not listed here is unlikely. Information has been obtained from the prints themselves, copper plates, drawings, and photographs, from the artist's business and personal records and copies of his correspondence, from published articles, books, and critical essays, and from many gracious individuals who have provided valuable material and helped verify data. Where different sources have yielded contradictory information, we have noted the contradictions and left the ultimate resolution to future scholars.

In this catalogue, each print is described by number, title, medium, date, dimensions, and size of edition and number of known proofs. In some instances, additional information is included to explain unusual circumstances that need to be understood to assure positive identification of a particular print. When the title does not indicate the geographic location of the subject, the location has been identified and noted as part of the description of the print. Two hundred and two of Chamberlain's prints have European subjects, seventy-nine have American subjects, four are imaginary, and a single print is of a North African scene. Of the European subjects, one hundred and forty-seven are French, twenty-three are Italian, eighteen are English, twelve are Spanish, and two are Belgian. The index "Prints by Location of the Subject" provides the reader with a more specific location, whenever possible, for the subject matter of each Chamberlain print.

The place where the artist was working when a given plate or stone was executed is not stated because the reader can deduce this information from the section called "Chronology of the Artist's Life" or from Chamberlain's autobiography, *Etched in Sunlight*. The noteworthy point is that, although the artist often engraved a plate directly from nature or in the locale of the scene depicted, occasionally he worked on American subjects in France or European subjects in America.

THE NUMBERING OF PRINTS has been arranged to group those made for similar purposes while maintaining a sense of chronology. Chamberlain numbered prints in his own catalogue according to the month and year in which he completed them. As previously mentioned, he catalogued only those that he intended to publish and sell through his dealers. We have retained the numbers for these prints that they always have had. This group, "The Artist's Catalogue of Prints Intended for Publication," comprises entries No. 1 through No. 132. Even though each of the following three prints could be classified in another group, we have chosen to leave them where they were listed by Chamberlain in order to keep their original numbers: No. 78, *Kansas City War Memorial*, was privately commissioned by Mr. J. H. Bender of Kansas City, Missouri; No. 96, *Gateway in the Ghetto, Paris*, was used as the frontispiece for a special edition of the book *France Will Live Again*; and No. 116, *The Abandoned Chateau*, was engraved further, many years after its publication, to demonstrate the process of drypoint to a gathering at the Club of Odd Volumes in Boston.

In Chamberlain's catalogue were recorded, as well, eleven prints of Williamsburg, Virginia, numbered with the letter "W" before Arabic numerals one through eleven. We have grouped these prints with the others from the artist's catalogue, but we have renumbered them, omitting the letter designation and continuing with consecutive Arabic numerals from the last entry of the preceding group. These prints have the numbers 133 through 143. We assigned the number 144 to an unprinted, untitled plate that depicts a scene in Williamsburg, Virginia. Consequently, entries No. 133 through No. 144 form the group "Drypoints of Williamsburg, Virginia."

Entries No. 145 through No. 203 form a group titled "Prints Considered Unpublished." These prints were engraved to demonstrate the processes of printmaking, to experiment, or for unusual purposes. Chamberlain considered all prints in this group unpublished, even though records show that as many as thirty proofs exist of some of these prints.

Entries No. 204 through 208 comprise the group "Five Large Lithographs." These prints have dimensions more in the tradition of lithographic posters than the smaller sizes that characterize Chamberlain's other lithographs.

The seven remaining groups have self-explanatory titles; however, a privately commissioned print, No. 200, *Lydia Pinkham Compound Label*, is not listed with the group "Privately Commissioned Prints." We preferred to list it with others that were made for unusual purposes in the group "Prints Considered Unpublished."

TITLES have been taken from the artist's records, from titles written by the artist on catalogue proofs, from titles of drawings of the same subject and design, or from titles over which prints have been reproduced in Chamberlain's books or other publications. When reproductions have been the only source for nomenclature, we have given prints the titles over which we found them reproduced and have noted the published sources in relevant numbered entries of the appendix "Notes on Printing and Publishing." Titles of some prints are in French. A French title usually indicates that the print was published in France. Titles of the remaining prints are in English, and these were published in either England or the United States.

Sometimes a print appears in the artist's records and publications over different titles. In these instances we have catalogued the print by the title most frequently used by the artist, or the one that our research has shown may be more logical. For example, we have verified that the setting of the subject for Prints No. 188 and No. 202 is the English village of Pembridge, but No. 188 has been reproduced in Chamberlain's books sometimes over the title *Pembridge* and other times, *Pembroke*. We have chosen to assign the title *Pembridge* to print No. 188. The other print depicting a scene in the village of Pembridge appears only over the title *Pembroke*, which is the reason that this print, No. 202, retains the title *Pembroke* in our cataloguing. Some of the publications in which alternate but less frequently used titles for a single print have been found are cited in relevant numbered entries of the appendix "Notes on Printing and Publishing." These alternate titles, along with the preferred titles and catalogue numbers, are listed in the index "Titles of the Prints, with Print Numbers and Metric Measurements."

Seventeen prints remain untitled because we found no data to indicate titles for them. These prints are identified by a catalogue number and a brief description of the subject. They have the following numbers: 144, 158, 170 through 183, 190, and 195 through 198.

A few prints share the same titles. Two prints have the title *An Alley in Pont Audemer*: a drypoint, No. 134, and a lithograph, No. 145. Three prints, Nos. 161, 162, and 163, share the title *Farm Gate in the Oise* and depict the same subject and design in different media. No. 161 is a drypoint, No. 162, an etching, and No. 163, a soft-ground etching. Two etchings share the title *The Fortress, Carmona*. They are numbered 165 and 166. These prints are mirror image designs of the same subject.

Three prints are known to us only through reproductions. They are the following: No. 150, *Dijon*; No. 151, *The Plaza, Baza, Spain*; and No. 152, *The Ponte Vecchio, Florence*. Reproductions of these prints accompanied the original publication of Chamberlain's essay "Lithographic Processes in Architectural Illustration." A credit line accompanying the essay identifies these illustrations as reproductions of lithographs by Samuel Chamberlain.

The MEDIUM of each print has been ascertained from inspecting proofs and plates and from information in the artist's records and published works. Of Chamberlain's two hundred and eighty-six prints, one hundred and sixty-two are drypoints; sixty-six are etchings, including several soft-ground etchings, a few aquatints, and an etching with mezzotint; and fifty-eight are lithographs.

Of nine unfinished plates, seven were planned for drypoint and two for etching. All nine have no catalogue numbers, but have been given letter designations and are described in the appendix "Unfinished Plates."

Chamberlain's etchings and drypoints can be presumed to have been engraved on copper except those noted in this catalogue as having been engraved on zinc. All of the artist's lithographs were printed from stone.

The DATE given in each entry is that of the completion of the plate or stone as stated in the artist's records, the date of publication of the print, the copyright date of the print, or the approximate date of completion, deduced from publication dates of books, portfolios, or periodicals in which a particular print appeared. Approximate dates for completion of some prints have been inferred from references to these works in the artist's autobiography, business records, and correspondence.

DIMENSIONS of each print are given in inches, to the nearest sixteenth, with height preceding width. Height has been measured at the left-hand side and width at the lower edge of each plate or image. The dimensions of each etching or drypoint include the mark of the bevel of the plate. Each lithograph has been measured from the extremities of the image.

Chamberlain used the U.S. customary (English) system of measurement to record dimensions of his prints, and we have retained the same system in our cataloguing. However, the artist's international reputation, as well as increasing use of the International (Metric) system of measurements in the United States, warrants the inclusion of metric dimensions for the prints in this volume. Metric equivalents were obtained by converting the English measurements rather than by measuring each print with a metric scale. Dimensions in centimeters to the nearest tenth, with height preceding width, can be found for each print in the index "Titles of the Prints, with Print Numbers and Metric Measurements."

THE SIZE OF EDITIONS and number of proofs of each print have been determined from many of the sources previously enumerated in these pages as well as the usual one of hand-written fractions or other notations just below the plate mark on the left-hand side of many proofs. Discrepancies concerning the number of proofs in editions of some prints are explained in relevant entries of the appendix "Notes on Printing and Publishing."

Two editions have been printed from each of the following three plates: No. 134, *The Capitol, Williamsburg*; No. 135, *The Governor's Palace, Williamsburg*; and No. 136, *The Raleigh Tavern, Williamsburg*. Three editions have been printed of No. 133, and each edition has a different title. The first edition is called *The Apothecary's Shop, Williamsburg*; the second, *The Printing Office, Williamsburg*; and the third, *The Duke of Gloucester Street, Williamsburg*. All three editions have been referred to by the title *The Apothecary's Shop, Williamsburg*.

In our catalogue entries, the term "working proof" includes the usual trial proofs that the reader would expect to find here. In addition, the term includes a group of proofs that can be considered working proofs in a general sense, even though Chamberlain inscribed these proofs or referred to them by other nomenclature. He often labeled the few proofs printed from a plate at each stage of its development as proofs of states, spelling out "first," "second," or "third," and usually but not always designating the number of proofs in each of these states with Roman numerals or with notations like the following: "First state—only impression" or "Only first state." In his later years, Chamberlain frequently used the terms "state" and "trial proof" interchangeably. The particular proofs of each print that are encompassed by our term "working proof" are described in each pertinent entry of the appendix "Notes on Printing and Publishing." A single print, No. 102, *Slums of Rouen*, is the only one where differences between the stages of its development are described in the catalogue entry. Two of its five states have more than fifteen proofs each.

The section "Chronology of the Artist's Life" outlines important dates and events in Chamberlain's life and for a few years following his death. Obviously, some of this information is not recounted in the artist's autobiography, *Etched in Sunlight*, and many dates are not easy to deduce from this source. Nonetheless, his autobiography remains the reader's primary source for studying the artist's history.

The essays by Narcissa Gellatly Chamberlain, Walter Muir Whitehill, Sinclair Hamilton Hitchings, and June and Norman Kraeft have been edited from those printed in the catalogue of the memorial exhibition of Samuel Chamberlain's drawings and prints, held at The Octagon, Washington, D.C. This exhibition was organized by the Kraefts under the sponsorship of The American Institute of Architects Foundation, Washington, D.C., and the Boston Public Library, Boston, Massachusetts. These commentaries, tributes to Samuel Chamberlain the man and printmaker, serve to introduce the artist to the reader.

The three essays in the section "Printmaking According to Chamberlain" were written by the artist early in his career and published in the periodical *The American Architect*. These articles are reprinted here in their entirety.

In the section "The Prints," each of Chamberlain's prints is catalogued numerically and described as previously noted by title, medium, date, dimensions, and number of proofs.

The appendices provide additional information about the artist and his works. In the appendix "Unfinished Plates," nine unfinished copper plates that were found in the artist's studio after his death and remain untitled are each described. The appendix "Notes on Printing and Publishing" already has been called to the reader's attention. In this appendix, particular data about individual prints is recorded and catalogued in numerical sequence by catalogue number and title.

The appended list "Books and Portfolios Written or Illustrated by Samuel Chamberlain" provides complete bibliographical information for each book; consequently, throughout our catalogue when referring to books authored by the artist, we have stated only the title.

The list "Collections in Museums and Other Institutions Containing Prints by Samuel Chamberlain" may be incomplete. We made inquiries to locate the artist's prints in collections that are accessible to the public. The resulting list testifies to the national and international interest in Chamberlain's prints. At present, the collection with the greatest number of the artist's prints is the Wiggin Collection at the Boston Public Library. Another comprehensive collection is housed in the Essex Institute, Salem, Massachusetts.

Two lists "Awards and Decorations" and "Memberships" further attest to the variety of interests that Samuel Chamberlain pursued throughout his long and productive life.

The several particular indices have been compiled and included especially to facilitate the reader's research of individual prints.

J.F.K.

THE PRINTS

NOS. 1–132

The following one hundred and thirty-two entries describe prints noted in the artist's records as published and those intended for publication, although some were later abandoned and considered by the artist to be unpublished.

1. *A Side Street in Beauvais*, etching, 1925, 13¼ x 9¼, edition of 100, as well as 2 working proofs.

2. *Notre Dame from the Quai de l'Hôtel de Ville*, etching, 1925, 10³/₄ x 11³/₄, edition of 100.
The print also is known by the title *Île-de-la-Cité, Paris*.

3. *The Blacksmith's Shop, Senlis*, etching, 1925, 8⁷/₈ x 11¹/₈, about 23 proofs.

4. *Old Houses in Rouen*, etching, 1925, 9⁷/₈ x 7¹/₂, about 13 proofs.

5. *The Loggia di Lanzi, Florence*, etching, 1925, 11¹¹/₁₆ x 7¹¹/₁₆, about 35 proofs.

6. *Taormina*, etching, 1925, 10⁷/₈ x 7, 21 proofs, including a single artist's proof.

7. *The Buttresses of Beauvais Cathedral*, etching, 1925, 8½ x 5, edition of 100, as well as 3 artist's proofs.

8. *Amalfi*, etching, 1925, 7 x 7, edition of 100, as well as a single working proof.

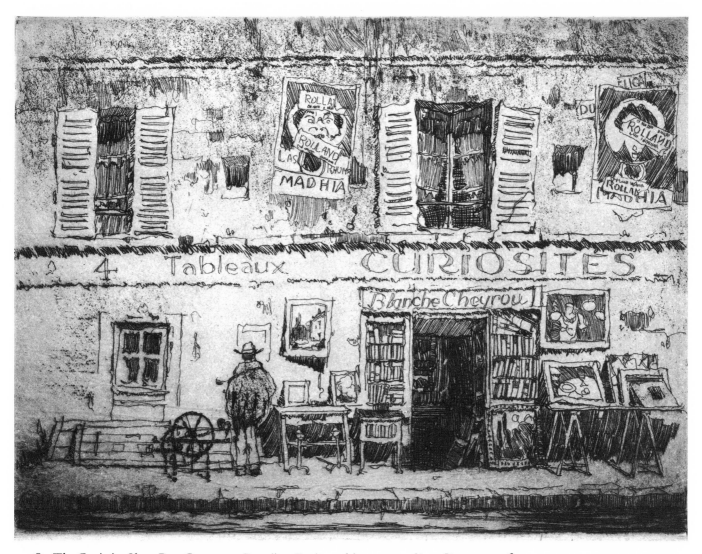

9. *The Curiosity Shop, Rue Campagne Première, Paris,* etching, 1925, 5¹/₈ x 7⁷/₁₆, 33 proofs.

10. *Church of San Giovanni Battiste, Siracusa*, etching, 1925, 5¹/₂ x 6⁵/₁₆, about 36 proofs.

11. *Church of Saint Ayoul, Provins*, etching, 1925, $5^{13}/_{16}$ x $7^3/_4$, 69 proofs, including a single artist's proof.

12. *The Church at Sézanne*, etching, 1925, 7⁹/₁₆ X 3³/₄,
edition of 100.

13. *Semur-en-Auxois*, etching, 1925, 6¼ x 9¼, about 35 proofs, including 2 working proofs and a single artist's proof.

14. *A Gateway in Seville*, etching, 1925, 8 x 5¹/₄, 35 proofs, including 3 working proofs.

15. *Gateway of Santa Maria, Burgos,* etching, 1925, 6 x 4³/₄, about 38 proofs, including a single working proof.

16. *House on the River, Albi,* etching, 1925, $5^7/_8$ x $4^1/_8$,
20 proofs.

17. *Old Houses in Lisieux*, soft-ground etching, spring 1925, 7³/₈ x 4⁵/₈, 29 proofs, including a single artist's proof.

18. *The Cypresses, Siracusa*, soft-ground etching, 1925, 7¼ x 8⅜, about 61 proofs, including a single artist's proof.

19. *The Giant Buttress, Bourges*, soft-ground etching, 1925, 7$\frac{1}{2}$ x 5$\frac{1}{2}$, about 16 proofs, including 2 working proofs.

20. *The Fish Market, Chartres,* soft-ground etching, 1925, 7^3/$_{16}$ x 10^7/$_8$, about 49 proofs, including 2 artist's proofs.

21. *Springtime in Senlis*, drypoint, 1925, 7¹¹/₁₆ x 9⅛, edition of 20, as well as 3 working proofs.

22. *Rue Daubenton, Paris*, drypoint, early 1925, 9¹/₈ x 5⁷/₈, about 15 proofs.

23. *The Bridge of Pinos, Spain*, drypoint, 1925, 3⁵/₈ x 5¹/₈, about 16 proofs, including a single artist's proof.

24. *The Beach, Minori*, drypoint, 1925, 8¹⁄₈ x 6¹⁄₂, about 19 proofs, including a single working proof. An untitled etching, No. 176, mirror image of the same subject and design, was engraved in 1925 and measures 9³⁄₄ x 7.

25. *Rue Mouffetard, Paris*, lithograph, 1925, $9^7/_8$ x $15^1/_4$, edition of 35.

26. *The Cloister, Saint Benoît*, lithograph, 1925, 4 x 7½, about 25 proofs.

27. *The Tower in Andujar*, lithograph, 1925, 13⅛ x 9¼, 25 proofs.

28. *Châteaudun*, lithograph, 1925, 7$\frac{1}{8}$ x 9$\frac{3}{4}$, 26 proofs, including a catalogue proof.

29. *The Chateau in the Lot*, lithograph, 1925, 3¹/₂ x 7¹/₄, edition of 25.

30. *Gateway in Perpignan*, lithograph, 1925, 11¹/₈ x 7¹/₈, edition of 20.

31. *Montrichard in May*, drypoint, January 1926, $6^{1}/_{4}$ x $4^{7}/_{8}$, edition of 20, as well as 2 artist's proofs.

32. *The Farm Gate, Virolet*, drypoint on zinc, July 1926, $7^1/8$ x $5^1/16$,
edition of 25. The print also is known by the title
The Farmyard Door, Virolet.

33. *The Poplars*, drypoint on zinc, July 1926, 5^1/$_8$ x 6^7/$_8$, about 18 proofs, including a single working proof. The subject is a scene in the Île-de-France.

34. *An Alley in Pont Audemer*, drypoint on zinc, August 1926, 8³/₄ x 5⁷/₈, about 8 proofs, including a single working proof. A lithograph, print No. 145, has the same title.

35. *Vitré*, drypoint, September 1926, 4 x 5⁷/₈, edition of 75, as well as 2 working proofs, 2 artist's proofs, and a few proofs printed from the canceled plate.

36. *The Kitchen Door*, drypoint, July 1926, 4¹/₂ x 6¹/₈, edition of 60, as well as a single artist's proof. The setting of the subject is a scene in Vernon, France.

37. *The Winding Road, Vernon*, drypoint, August 1926, 5⅝ x 8, edition of 50, as well as a single artist's proof.

38. *The Porches, Dinan*, drypoint, September 1926, 8¼ x 5⅞, edition of 50, as well as a working proof, an artist's proof, and a few proofs printed from the canceled plate. The print also is known by the title *Old Houses, Dinan*.

39. *Remnants of Gothic Lace Work, Pont Audemer*, drypoint,
August 1926, 9 x 4¹/₂, edition of 50, as well as 1 or 2 working
proofs, a few artist's proofs, and a few proofs printed
from the canceled plate.

THE VALLEY IN VITRÉ

40. *The Valley in Vitré*, lithograph, 1926, 6 x 11, a few artist's proofs and a catalogue proof.

PONT AUDEMER

artist proof

JCC

41. *Pont Audemer*, lithograph, 1926, 11⅛ x 8, a few proofs, including an artist's proof and a catalogue proof.

42. *Vieilles Maisons, Dinan*, lithograph, 1927, 7$\frac{1}{2}$ x 10$\frac{1}{2}$, edition of 35, as well as a single artist's proof.

THE FARM GATE

43. *The Farm Gate, Vernonnet*, lithograph, July 1926, 9½ x 13¼, about 15 proofs. Some proofs, printed contre-collé, measure 10⅝ x 14³⁄₁₆.

THE SPIRES OF COUTANCES

44. *The Spires of Coutances*, lithograph, September 1926, $15^3/4$ x $9^3/4$, about 11 proofs.

45. *The Village Church, Menilles,* drypoint on zinc, August 1926, 7 x 5¹/₈, 15 proofs, including a catalogue proof and a few proofs printed from the canceled plate.

46. *The Quais, Saint Tropez*, drypoint, February 1927, 4¼ x 5¾, edition of 75, as well as 3 working proofs.

47. *The Hilltop, Villefranche-sur-Mer*,
drypoint, December 1926, 4³⁄₈ x 5,
edition of 60, as well as
3 working proofs and
a single artist's proof.

48. *The Waterfront, Villefranche-sur-Mer*, drypoint, January 1927, 5¹⁄₈ x 7,
edition of 75, as well as 3 working proofs.

49. *The Battered Boat, Villefranche-sur-Mer*, drypoint, January 1927, 4³/₈ x 6⁵/₁₆, edition of 75, as well as 3 working proofs and 2 artist's proofs.

50. *Old Menton*, drypoint, March 1927, 7 x 5¹/₁₆, edition of 75, as well as
a few proofs printed from the canceled plate. The print also is known
by the title *A Menton Gateway*.

51. *The Sheltered Street, Vitré*, lithograph, September 1926, 9¼ x 12¾, about 15 proofs.
The print also is known by the title *The Porches, Vitré*.

52. *Petite Venise, Colmar*, drypoint, May 1927, 5 x 6⅞, edition of 60, as well as 2 working proofs, 2 artist's proofs, and a catalogue proof. The print also has been reproduced over the title *Little Venice*.

53. *Broom Shop, Lucca*, lithograph, August 1927, 5^{13}/$_{16}$ x 9^{1}/$_{8}$, edition of 50.

54. *Cathedral Spires, Angers*, drypoint, July 1927, 9¹/₈ x 5¹/₂, edition of 75, as well as a single working proof and 5 artist's proofs. The working proof has dimensions larger than all other proofs, although its actual size is not known.

55. *The Veterans, Josselin*, drypoint, September 1927, 4⁵/₁₆ x 7¹³/₁₆, edition of 75.

56. *Fishing Boats, Menton*, lithograph, May 1927, 8½ x 16½, about 7 proofs. The
print also is known by the title *The Harbor, Menton*.

57. *Menton Tenements*, lithograph, May 1927, 8½ x 16½, 16 proofs.

58. *Colmar*, lithograph, May 1927, 13^{1}/$_{2}$ x 8^{7}/$_{8}$, 11 proofs. The print also is known by the title *The Market Place, Colmar*.

59. *Porte du Vieux Pont, Sospel*, lithograph, January 1928, 6 x 9, edition of 50, as well as a single artist's proof. Print No. 193, *The Bridge at Sospel*, a drypoint, is of the same subject and similar design.

60. *Siena*, drypoint, January 1928,
    12^1/$_4$ x 6^3/$_{16}$, edition of 100,
    as well as 3 artist's proofs.

61. *Tunis,* aquatint, January 1928, 8³/₄ x 5¹/₂, about 10 proofs, including a few
working proofs in black and several proofs in predominantly blue and
sienna-colored inks.

62. *Gables of Colmar*, drypoint, March 1928, 7¹³/₁₆ x 10³/₄, edition of 100, as well as 3 working proofs and 2 artist's proofs.

63. *Plaza de San Martin, Segovia*, drypoint, March 1928, 6⁵/₁₆ x 7³/₄, edition of 100, as well as a single working proof and an artist's proof.

64. *Perugia*, drypoint, April 1928, 12¹/₂ x 7³/₄, edition of 100, as well as 2 working proofs and 3 artist's proofs.

65. *Cour du Marché, Bruges*, drypoint, June 1928, 8⁷/₈ x 6⁷/₈, edition of 100, as well as a single working proof.

66. *The Sunlit Tower, Colmar*,
drypoint, May 1928,
13$\frac{1}{2}$ x 9$\frac{1}{8}$, edition of 100,
as well as 4 working
proofs and 5 artist's proofs.

67. *Sailors Home from the Sea*, drypoint, August 1928, 6⅞ x 9⅞, edition of 100, as well as 3 artist's proofs. The subject is a scene in Étretat, Normandy.

68. *Broad Street, Ludlow*, drypoint, June 1928, 7⅝ x 9⅞, edition of 100.

69. *Canterbury*, drypoint, July 1928, 9 x 6⅝, edition of 100, as well as a single working proof and 2 artist's proofs. The print also is known by the title *High Street, Canterbury*.

70. *A Stable Court in Essex*, drypoint, July 1928, 7¹/₈ x 9¹/₂, edition of 100, as well as a single working proof and 5 artist's proofs.

71. *Founders' Tower, Magdalen College, Oxford*, drypoint, August 1928, 11 x 7¹/₁₆, edition of 100.

72. *An Umbrian Gateway*, lithograph, May 1928, 8⅝ x 6⅜, about 16 proofs. The print also is known by the title *Gate near Orvieto*.

73. *Harness Shop*, drypoint, March 1928, 4$^{15}/_{16}$ x 6, edition of 50, as well as 4 artist's proofs. The subject is a scene in a Normandy village.

74. *Lucca*, lithograph, May 1928, 9⅝ x 6⅛, edition of 25.

75. *Salamanca Cathedral*, drypoint, April 1929, 10³/₄ x 7¹/₈, edition of 100, as well as about 6 working proofs and 4 artist's proofs.

76. *Hôpital Saint Jean, Bruges*, drypoint, April 1929, $8^{1}/_{4}$ x $9^{1}/_{8}$, edition of 100, as well as 5 working proofs and a few artist's proofs.

77. *Far West Junk Shop*, drypoint, May 1929, 4⅝ x 8¾, edition of 100, as well as
4 working proofs and a few artist's proofs. The working proofs measure 6⅜ x 9³⁄₁₆.
The setting of the subject is a West Coast town in the United States.

78. *Kansas City War Memorial*, drypoint, June 1929, 6¼ x 8¾, about 10 proofs, including 2 working proofs and a single artist's proof.

79. *Soaring Steel*, drypoint, July 1929, 12¹/₂ x 9⁵/₈, edition of 125, as well as 4 working proofs, a few artist's proofs, and a catalogue proof. The subject is the Daily News Building, Chicago, Illinois.

80. *Oil*, drypoint, July 1929, 9$\frac{1}{2}$ x 6$\frac{5}{8}$, 30 proofs, including a few working proofs, a single artist's proof, and a catalogue proof. The setting of the subject is an oil field in California.

81. *Manhattan, Old and New*, drypoint, July 1929, 9 x 7⅛, edition of 100, as well as about 5
working proofs, 4 artist's proofs, and a catalogue proof. The print also is known
by the title *New York, Ancien et Nouveau*.

82. *Boston Fish Pier*, drypoint, June 1929, 5⅝ x 8⅝, edition of 100, as well as an artist's proof, a catalogue proof, and 4 working proofs from the uncropped plate, measuring 6½ x 8⅝.

83. *Faneuil Hall, Boston*, drypoint, August 1929, 6¹/₄ x 9, edition of 100, as well as 4 working proofs and a catalogue proof.

84. *Drizzly Morning in Chicago*, drypoint, September 1929, 4 x 7¹/₂, edition of 100, as well as 2 working proofs and a catalogue proof.

85. *The Customs Tower, Boston*, drypoint, August 1929, 5⅝ x 8, 15 proofs,
including 2 working proofs, 5 artist's proofs, and a catalogue proof.

86. *The Curving Canyon, New York*, drypoint, September 1929, 8⅞ x 5⅞, 65 proofs, including 2 working proofs, 2 artist's proofs, and a catalogue proof.

87. *Grain Elevators*, drypoint, August 1929, 6¼ x 10³/₁₆, edition of 100, as well as 2 working proofs and a catalogue proof. The subject is a scene near Minneapolis, Minnesota.

88. *Verneuil*, drypoint, November 1929, 13³/₄ x 8¹/₂, edition of 100,
as well as 8 working proofs, 5 artist's proofs, and a catalogue proof.

89. *La-Charité-sur-Loire*, drypoint, January 1930, 11 x 7½, edition of 100, as well as 7 working proofs and 3 artist's proofs. Many of the working proofs measure 11¾ x 8½, because the plate was cropped from the top and right late in its development.

90. *Market Day in Lillebonne*, drypoint, January 1930, 13³/₄ x 9¹/₈, edition of 100, as well as about 5 artist's proofs.

91. *Auxerre*, drypoint, January 1930, 6¹/₈ x 8¹/₂, edition of 75, as well as 4 working proofs.

92. *Dentelles Gothiques, Clamecy*, drypoint, February 1930, 15¹/₈ x 10¹/₈, edition of 100, as well as 6 working proofs and 4 artist's proofs.

93. *Cathedral of Sens*, drypoint, March 1930, 10³/₄ x 7¹/₈, edition of 100, as well as 5 working proofs.

94. *Skyscrapers of Menton*, drypoint, April 1930, 12⅝ x 9½, edition of 100, as well as 6 working proofs.

95. *Towers of Senlis,* drypoint, 1930, 10 x 7¼, edition of 100, as well as 7 working proofs. The second working proof has pencil-drawn additions, including a tree above the wall on the left-hand side of the print. These changes were engraved on the plate before the remaining proofs were printed.

96. *Gateway in the Ghetto, Paris*, drypoint, June 1930, $7^5/8$ x $4^7/8$, edition of 100, as well as 5 working proofs and 3 artist's proofs.

97. *Midsummer Silhouette*, working proofs. The first working proof
reproduced here has the same image size as later proofs,
but the inked area is slightly narrower.

97. *Midsummer
Silhouette*, working
proof before plate was
scraped to produce the
sharper and clearer
lines of the edition
proof below.

97. *Midsummer Silhouette*, drypoint, June 1930, 5⁷/₈ x 5³/₄,
edition of 75, as well as 5 working proofs and a few
artist's proofs. The subject is a scene near Senlis.

98. *The Shadowy Street*, drypoint, July 1930, 4⁷/₈ x 4¹/₂, edition of 75, as well as 4 working proofs. The subject is a scene in Senlis.

99. *Fruit Store Façade*, drypoint, August 1930, 4⁵/₈ x 6¹³/₁₆, edition of 75, as well as a few working proofs. Some working proofs measure 9 x 6¹³/₁₆, because the plate was cropped later in the development of the print. A single proof has been tinted with watercolors. The subject is a scene in Senlis.

100. *Place Notre Dame, Senlis*, drypoint, August 1930, $5^3/_8$ x $5^7/_8$, edition of 75, as well as 4 working proofs.

101. *The Mason's House, Senlis,* drypoint, September 1930, 10³/₈ x 8, edition of 100, as well as 4 working proofs.

102. *Slums of Rouen*, drypoint, September 1930. A set of 4 working proofs, measuring 9⁷/₁₆ x 6⁵/₈, precedes a third state of 17 proofs, which have the same measurements. The fourth state is of 18 proofs measuring 8¹/₄ x 6⁵/₈. A single final proof is inscribed "fifth state." Before the proofs of the fourth state were printed, the plate was cropped at the bottom, and a shadow was engraved over the remaining depiction of cobblestones in the foreground. More lines were engraved to soften some details of the previous state. The final proof shows further engraving and reworking of the plate before the artist abandoned it.

103. *Porte Saint Guillaume, Chartres*, drypoint, October 1930, $7^{13}/_{16}$ x $6^{1}/_{16}$, edition of 100, as well as 3 working proofs.

CHARTRES CATHEDRAL

Gift of the artist - June 1960

Chartres Cathedral, pencil drawing, study for 104.

104. *Chartres Cathedral*, drypoint, working proof.

104. *Chartres Cathedral*, drypoint, working proof.

104. *Chartres Cathedral*, drypoint, February 1931, 14³/₈ x 9⁷/₈, edition of 100, as well as 3 working proofs and 5 artist's proofs. The first 2 working proofs were printed from the untrimmed plate, 14³/₈ x 10¹¹/₁₆. The size of the image remains the same throughout the printing.

105. *Beauvais*, drypoint, working proof.

105. *Beauvais*, drypoint, April 1931, 11⁵/₁₆ x 12¹/₄, edition of 100, as well as a few working proofs and a few artist's proofs.

106. *Silhouette of Senlis*, drypoint, June 1931, 5⁷/₈ x 8¹/₂, edition of 100, as well as 5 working proofs.

107. *The Verdant Village*, drypoint, July 1931, 6¹/₂ x 11, edition of 100, as well as 6 working proofs. The setting of the subject is Bellefontaine, Île-de-France.

108. *The Saplings*, drypoint, August 1931, 7¹/₂ x 10¹/₈, edition of 100, as well as 5 working proofs. The subject is a scene in Île-de-France.

109. *The Abbey Farm*, drypoint, September 1931, 7³/₄ x 10¹/₄, edition of 100, as well as 3 working proofs. The setting of the subject is Breuil-le-Vert, Île-de-France.

110. *Senlis from a Crow's Nest*, drypoint, November 1931, 11³/₈ x 9⁵/₈, edition of 100, as well as 4 working proofs. One working proof measures 13³/₄ x 11¹/₈, because it was printed before the plate was cut to its present dimensions. The print also is known by the title *Senlis from a Bird's Nest*.

111. *Manhattan Twilight*, etching with mezzotint, May 1932, 13⁵/₁₆ x 9¹/₂, edition of 100, as well as a series of 14 working proofs, which evolved through nine stages of development.

112. *Espalion*, drypoint, working proofs.

112. *Espalion*, drypoint, May 1933, 6¹/₄ x 10³/₄, edition of 75, as well as about 8 working proofs and a single artist's proof. When the first proofs were printed, the plate measured 8 x 11⁷/₈. The additional proofs were printed from the cropped plate, although the size of the image remained the same on all proofs.

113. *Lisieux*, drypoint, June 1933, $6^7/_8$ x 11, edition of 75, as well as a few working proofs. Three working proofs measure $11^1/_8$ x $13^{13}/_{16}$. The plate was cropped to $7^1/_2$ x $13^3/_{16}$, and a single proof was printed. After further cropping, some additional working proofs and the edition were printed.

114. *Albi Sunset*, drypoint, October 1933, 9³/₈ x 11⁵/₁₆, edition of 100, as well as 7 working proofs and 3 artist's proofs. Several proofs were printed before the plate was cut from 11¹/₈ x 13⁷/₈ to its final dimensions. However, the size of the image remained the same throughout the printing.

115. *The Country Road*, drypoint, October 1933, 8 x 10³/₈, edition of 75, as well as 3 working proofs and 3 artist's proofs. The subject is a scene near Saint Firmin, Île-de-France.

116. *The Abandoned Chateau*, drypoint, August 1934, $7^{15}/_{16}$ x $9^{3}/_{4}$, edition of 100, as well as 10 or 11 working proofs. The plate was engraved further in February 1940, and a few additional proofs were printed. The setting of the subject is Fougères, Touraine.

117. *The Abbey of Montmajour*, drypoint, September 1934, 11³/₈ x 8¹/₈, edition of 75, as well as 2 working proofs and 3 artist's proofs. The abbey is near Arles, France.

118. *Quimper*, drypoint, working proofs.

118. *Quimper*, drypoint, June 1935, 14⅝ x 8¾, edition of 100, as well as 9 working proofs and 5 artist's proofs. The proofs reproduced here were described by the artist as "Only First State," "Only Second State," and "3rd State."

119. *The Giant Oak*, drypoint, November 1935, 8⁷/₁₆ x 10, edition of 100, as well as 3 working proofs and 5 artist's proofs. The subject is a scene near Fairfield, Connecticut.

120. *Burgundy Hillside*, drypoint, November 1935, 8¹⁵/₁₆ x 11, edition of 100, as well as 3 working proofs and 2 artist's proofs. The subject is a scene in La Rochepot.

121. *Essex Village*, drypoint, January 1936, 6¹/₈ x 11⁵/₈, edition of 100, as well as 2 working proofs. The setting of the subject is Newport, Essex, England.

122. *Noon in Noyers*, drypoint, January 1936, 7³/₈ x 8⁷/₈, edition of 100, as well as 6 working proofs. Two proofs, measuring 7⁵/₈ x 10¹/₈, were printed before the plate was cropped to its present dimensions.

123. *Summer Street, Marblehead*, drypoint, February 1936, 9¼ x 7⅛, edition of 100, as well as 4 working proofs and a few artist's proofs.

124. *Stonington Sunset*, drypoint, March 1936, 9⁷/₈ x 14⁵/₈, edition of 100, as well as 10 working proofs and a few artist's proofs. The setting of the subject is Stonington, Connecticut.

125. *Saunderstown Fields*, drypoint, September 1936, 7¹/₈ x 10⁵/₈, edition of 100, as well as 5 working proofs and a few artist's proofs. The setting of the subject is Saunderstown, Rhode Island.

126. *Sunshine After Showers, the "Nantucket,"* drypoint, October 1937, 8³/₈ x 12¹/₂, about 25 proofs, including 5 working proofs and 4 or 5 artist's proofs. The setting of the subject is the Charlestown Naval Shipyard, Boston, Massachusetts.

127. *Springtime in Salem*, drypoint, April 1938, 8⁷/₈ x 12⁵/₈, edition of 100, as well as 9 working proofs. The setting of the subject is Chestnut Street, Salem, Massachusetts.

128. *The Rogers Building*, drypoint, June 1938, 12³/₁₆ x 9³/₁₆, edition of 100, as well as 8 working proofs. The Rogers Building was located in Boston, Massachusetts.

129. *Christ Church, Cambridge*, drypoint, October 1938, 12 x 9¼, edition of 100, as well as 2 working proofs and 5 artist's proofs. The subject is located in Cambridge, Massachusetts.

130. *Mediterranean Wash Day*, drypoint, January 1939, 8³/₄ x 12¹/₂, edition of 100, as well as 2 working proofs and a single artist's proof. The setting of the subject is Villefranche-sur-Mer.

131. *Bend in the Road*, drypoint, November 1940, 7¹/₂ x 13³/₈, edition of 100, as well as 5 working proofs. The subject is a scene in New Castle, New Hampshire.

132. *Valley of the Var*, drypoint, November 1940, 10⁷/₈ x 13³/₁₆, edition of 50, as well as 6 working proofs and a few artist's proofs. The setting of the subject is Entrevaux, France.

NOS. 133–144

The following twelve entries describe prints engraved of Williamsburg, Virginia, as it appeared after 1937, when the restoration of colonial Williamsburg was well advanced.

133. *The Apothecary's Shop, Williamsburg*, drypoint, June 1938, 9³/₈ x 7¹/₂, edition of 100, as well as 5 working proofs and 10 artist's proofs. The plate was engraved further at a later date, and a sign, "The Printing Office," was included in the composition. In March 1951, a second edition of 200 proofs was printed and given the title *The Printing Office, Williamsburg*. Late in 1973, a third edition of 100 proofs was printed and titled *The Duke of Gloucester Street, Williamsburg*. There are no discernable differences between the proofs of the second and third editions. All three have the same dimensions.

134. *The Capitol, Williamsburg*, drypoint, June 1938, 9⁷/₈ x 14¹/₂, edition of 100, as well as 4 working proofs and 5 artist's proofs. A second edition of 100 proofs was printed in the spring of 1969. No changes were engraved on the plate between the two editions, and the images of both have the same dimensions.

135. *The Governor's Palace, Williamsburg*, drypoint, August 1938, 10⅛ x 14⅝,
edition of 100, as well as a single working proof and 5 artist's proofs. A second
edition of 100 proofs was printed in the summer of 1969. No changes were engraved
on the plate between the two editions, and the images of both have the same dimensions.

136. *The Raleigh Tavern, Williamsburg*, drypoint, September 1938, $9^1/_2$ x $12^1/_8$, edition of 100, as well as a single working proof and 5 artist's proofs. A second edition of 100 proofs was printed in November 1968. No changes were engraved on the plate between these editions, and the images of both have the same dimensions.

137. *Bruton Parish Church, Williamsburg*, drypoint, October 1938, $10^{1}/_{2}$ x $7^{5}/_{8}$, edition of 100, as well as 3 working proofs and 10 artist's proofs.

138. *The Public Gaol, Williamsburg*, drypoint, December 1938, 8¹/₁₆ x 11¹/₄, edition of 100, as well as a single working proof and 5 artist's proofs.

139. *The Palace Gardens, Williamsburg*, drypoint, September 1939, 9⅝ x 13⅝, edition of 100, as well as a single working proof and 4 artist's proofs.

140. *Saint George Tucker House, Williamsburg*, drypoint, January 1940, 9⅝ x 7½,
edition of 100, as well as 7 working proofs and 5 artist's proofs.

141. *The Semple House, Williamsburg*, drypoint, August 1946, 8⁵/₈ x 7¹/₄, edition of 125, as well as 8 working proofs.

142. *The Wren Building, Williamsburg*, drypoint, c. 1947, 8¹/₂ x 12⁷/₈, about 15
proofs, including 11 working proofs.

143. *The Churchyard, Williamsburg*, drypoint, June 1948, 7¹/₄ x 9³/₈, edition of 200, as well as 5 working proofs.

144. Untitled (landscape in the neighborhood of the colonial building Sign of
the Golden Ball, Williamsburg, Virginia), drypoint, c. 1948, 7$\frac{1}{4}$ x 5$\frac{1}{4}$,
no known proofs.

NOS. 145–203

The following fifty-nine entries describe prints executed to experiment or to demonstrate engraving processes and lithographic techniques or for particularly unusual reasons. The number of proofs printed from most of these plates or stones is fewer than eight, although as many as thirty have been printed from some of them. Nevertheless, the artist considered these prints unpublished.

145. *An Alley in Pont Audemer*, lithograph, c. 1924, 9⅝ x 7½, a few proofs. The print also is known by the title *Courtyard in Beaune*. Print No. 34 also has the title *An Alley in Pont Audemer*, but depicts a different subject.

146. *Modena, Italy,* lithograph, c. 1924, 10$^{1}/_{16}$ x 8$^{1}/_{8}$, about 6 proofs.

147. *Fontana Grande, Viterbo*, lithograph, c. 1924, 6¹/₂ x 9⁷/₈, about 5 proofs.

148. *The Fountain, Viterbo*, lithograph, c. 1924, 6³/₄ x 11, about 6 proofs.

149. *Viterbo*, aquatint, c. 1924, 7 x 9⅝, about 8 proofs, including a few working proofs.

150. *Dijon*, lithograph, c. 1924, dimensions unknown, a single known proof.

151. *The Plaza, Baza, Spain*, lithograph, c. 1924, dimensions unknown, a single known proof.

152. *The Ponte Vecchio, Florence*, lithograph, c. 1924, dimensions unknown, a single known proof.

153. *Street Scene, Angers*, lithograph, c. 1924, 19⁷/₈ x 14³/₄, a single known proof.

154. *Pietrasanta, Italy*, lithograph, c. 1924, 10¹/₈ x 8¹/₄, about 5 proofs. Some
have highlights drawn in yellow ocher crayon.

155. *Pont Saint Bénézet, Avignon,* etching, c. 1924, 3³/₁₆ x 5³/₄, about 25 proofs.

156. *The Square, Pont Audemer,* lithograph, c. 1924, 7¹/₂ x 14¹/₄, about 5 proofs.
The print also is known by the title *Pont Audemer.*

157. *Vieux Saumur*, lithograph, c. 1924, 13⅝ x 10⅛, about 5 proofs. The print
also is known by the title *Old Saumur*.

158. Untitled (chateau of the "Ducs de Rohan," Josselin), drypoint, c. 1925, $5^1/_8$ x $6^{13}/_{16}$, a few proofs, including a few working proofs.

159. *A Chateau Farm near Siena*, drypoint, c. 1925, 5^{15}/$_{16}$ x 8^{7}/$_{8}$, about 7 proofs, including a single working proof.

160. *Château de Vitré*, lithograph, c. 1925, 11½ x 16, about 8 proofs.

161. *Farm Gate in the Oise*, drypoint, c. 1925, 7 x 5, a few proofs.

162. *Farm Gate in the Oise*, etching, c. 1925, 7 x 5, a few proofs.

163. *Farm Gate in the Oise*, soft-ground etching, c. 1925, 7 x 5, a few proofs.

164. *Farm Group in the Tuscan Hills*, etching, c. 1925, 5¹/₂ x 8¹/₂, about 5 proofs.

165. *The Fortress, Carmona*, etching, c. 1925, 3¹/₂ x 4⁹/₁₆, a few proofs.

166. *The Fortress, Carmona*, etching, c. 1925, 4 x 5¹/₂, a single proof. This print and the preceding one, No. 165, also are known by the title *Gateway in Spain*.

167. *The Market Place, Vernon*, etching, c. 1925, 9¹/₂ x 13⁵/₁₆, about 7 proofs, including 5 working proofs and a single artist's proof.

168. *Tower of a Church, Angoulême*, etching, c. 1925, 7 x 5¹⁵/₁₆, about 5 proofs.

169. *Town Gate, Rimini*, etching, c. 1925, $4^{15}/_{16}$ X $3^{15}/_{16}$, about 4 proofs.

170. Untitled (French building with old gas pump), drypoint, c. 1925, 7⁷/₈ x 9⁵/₈, a single known proof.

171. Untitled (French café and market, probably in Rouen), drypoint, c. 1925,
7¹³/₁₆ x 5⁹/₁₆, a single known proof.

172. Untitled (French hamlet with church tower), drypoint, c. 1925, $3^{15}/_{16}$ x $5^{7}/_{8}$, a few proofs.

173. Untitled (French street scene with clock tower), soft-ground etching,
c. 1925, 7 x 5³/₁₆, about 3 proofs.

174. Untitled (Roman aqueduct in Segovia, Spain),
etching, c. 1925, $5^5/8$ x $4^9/16$, a single known proof.

175. Untitled (street scene, probably in Paris), etching, c. 1925, 13³/₁₆ x 9⁹/₁₆, a single known proof.

176. Untitled (view of the beach, Minori), etching, c. 1925, 9³/₄ x 7, a few proofs, including 2 or 3 working proofs and a single artist's proof. The plate is a mirror image of and larger than No. 24, *The Beach, Minori*, a drypoint, which depicts the same subject and is of similar design.

177. Untitled (Verneuil street scene), soft-ground etching, c. 1925, 5¹/₁₆ x 4⁹/₁₆, a single known proof.

178. *Ann Arbor*, etching, 1926, 5¹/₂ x 4¹/₄, a few proofs, including a single working proof.

179. *Collegiate Sorosis House, Ann Arbor*, soft-ground etching, c. 1926, 4¹⁵⁄₁₆ x 6⁷⁄₈, a few proofs.

180. *Old Ann Arbor*, drypoint, 1926, 6 x 8⁷/₈, edition of 30.

181. *Old House on Liberty Street, Ann Arbor,* drypoint, 1926, 6¹/₂ x 9, edition of 30, as well as a single working proof.

182. *Phi Kappa Psi House, Ann Arbor*, etching, c. 1926, 4$^{15}/_{16}$ x 6$^{7}/_{8}$, a few proofs.

183. Untitled (Ann Arbor scene of an old wooden bridge in a meadow), drypoint,
c. 1926, 4 x 5⁷/₈, a few proofs.

184. *Les Oliviers, Menton*, drypoint, 1926, 7 x 5¹/₁₆, about 7 proofs.

185. *Le Paysage Breton*, drypoint, c. 1926, 8¹/₂ x 6¹/₄, about 7 proofs, including 3 working proofs. The subject is a scene in Brittany.

186. *The Hilltop, Kersey*, etching, summer 1928, 6 x 7⁵/₈, about 5 proofs.

187. *Long Wittenham, Oxfordshire*, soft-ground etching, summer 1928, 5¹/₈ x 7¹/₈, about 7 proofs.

188. *Pembridge*, etching, c. summer 1928, 5 x 7, about 7 proofs. The print has been reproduced over the title *Pembroke*. Print No. 202, *Pembroke*, is a design in drypoint of the same subject, engraved at a later date.

189. *Tewkesbury*, etching, c. summer 1928, 5 x 7, about 9 proofs.

190. Untitled (street scene in Kersey, England), drypoint,
c. summer 1928, $3^{15}/_{16}$ x $5^{13}/_{16}$, about 3 proofs.

191. *Farm Vista, Le Plessis-Luzarches*, drypoint, 1930, 8³/₈ x 6⁵/₈, about 20 proofs, including 4 working proofs. The print also is known by the title *The Farm Gate*.

192. *Place de la Concorde, Paris*, drypoint, July 1930, 8¼ x 6¼, about 25 proofs, as well as 3 working proofs measuring 10⅛ x 8.

193. *The Bridge at Sospel*, drypoint, c. 1934, 9¹/₈ x 11⁵/₈, about 5 proofs, including a single working proof.
Print No. 59, *Porte du Vieux Pont, Sospel*, a lithograph, is of the same subject and similar design.

194. *College Saint Vincent, Senlis*, drypoint, 1934, 4⁵/₁₆ x 5¹/₄, about 6 proofs.

195. Untitled (exercises in etching lines, a teaching plate), etching, c. 1934, 7¹/₈ x 5¹/₈, a few proofs.

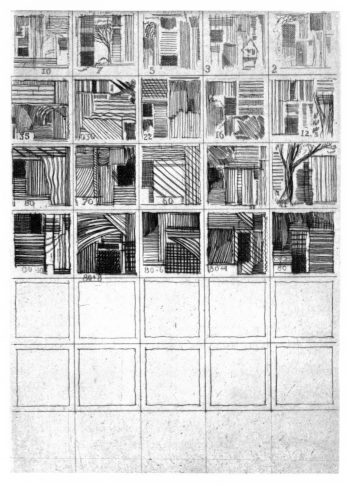

196. Untitled (houses along the quais, Paris), etching,
c. 1934, $6^{13}/_{16}$ x $4^{1}/_{2}$, about 5 proofs.

197. Untitled (a study of buildings on the Île-Saint-Louis, Paris), drypoint, c. 1934, 10⁵/₁₆ x 7¹⁵/₁₆, about 5 proofs.

198. Untitled (scene of Amalfi from the harbor, with an inscription on the right-hand side of the plate), etching, c. 1936, $4^3/_{16}$ x $5^{15}/_{16}$, no known proofs.

199. *New England Hill Town*, drypoint, 1937, 10¹⁄₈ x 13¹⁄₈, about 12 working proofs. The setting of the subject is Marblehead, Massachusetts.

200. *Lydia Pinkham Compound Label*, etching, c. 1939, 8³/₄ x 8¹/₄, a few proofs.

201. *Hooper Street*, soft-ground etching, June 1940, 7³/₄ x 5³/₁₆, about 15 proofs. The print also is known by the title *The King Hooper Mansion*. Print No. 274, an etching, also has the title *The King Hooper Mansion*. The subject is a scene in Marblehead, Massachusetts.

202. *Pembroke*, drypoint, June 1940, 4 x 5⁷/₈, a few proofs. The subject is a scene in the English village of Pembridge. Print No. 188, *Pembridge*, an etching, is of the same subject and similar design, but it was engraved at an earlier date.

203. *East Hagebourne, Berkshire*, drypoint, c. 1950, 5¹³/₁₆ x 7⁷/₈, about 5 proofs, including a single proof that was printed before the inscription "To Caroline" was engraved on the plate.

NOS. 204–208

The following five entries describe lithographs with unusually large dimensions.

204. *Ancien Couvent des Cordeliers, Paris,* lithograph, c. 1924, 20 x 14½, edition of 20 or 25.

205. *L'Église de Saint Étienne du Mont, Paris*, lithograph, c. 1924, 17$\frac{1}{2}$ x 11$\frac{1}{8}$, edition of 20.

206. *L'Église de Saint Nicolas de Chardonnet, Paris,* lithograph, c. 1924, 18 x 13, edition of 20 or 25.

207. *L'Horloge, Auxerre*, lithograph, c. 1924, 10⁷/₈ x 8³/₈, edition of 100.

208. *Rue Galande, Paris*, lithograph, c. 1924, 17¹/₂ x 10⁷/₈, edition of 20 or 25. The print also is known by the title *Rue Saint Julien-le-Pauvre*. The print No. 212, *L'Épicerie, Rue Galande, Paris*, also a lithograph, is of the same subject and similar design but has smaller dimensions, 15¹/₂ x 9¹/₂.

NOS. 209–228

The following twenty entries describe prints published as the portfolio Vingt Lithographies du Vieux Paris.

209. *Cour du Dragon, Paris*, lithograph, 1924, 13¹/₂ x 8¹/₂, edition of 100.

LE DÔME DE L'EGLISE DU VAL-DE-GRÂCE
PARIS   1924

210. *Le Dôme de l'Église du Val de Grâce, Paris,* lithograph, 1924, 16⅞ x 10¼, edition of 100.

211. *Échoppe d'Étameur, Paris*, lithograph, 1924, 11¹/₂ x 13¹/₄, edition of 100.

212. *L'Épicerie, Rue Galande, Paris*, lithograph, 1924, 15¹/₂ x 9¹/₂, edition of 100.
The print has been listed elsewhere by the title *L'Épicerie Rue Grande, Paris*.

213. *Fontaine de la Grosse Horloge, Rouen*, lithograph, 1924, 17 x 11, edition of 100.

214. *L'Horloge, Paris*, lithograph, 1924, 14$\frac{1}{2}$ x 8$\frac{3}{4}$, edition of 100.

215. *La Maison du Saumon, Chartres*, lithograph, 1924, 13¼ x 11, edition of 100.

216. *Maison de la Tourelle, Rue des Francs Bourgeois, Paris,* lithograph, 1924, 14½ x 10¼, edition of 100.

217. *Passy Ancien et Nouveau, Paris,* lithograph, 1924, 12½ x 11¼, edition of 100.

218. *Un Portail de l'Église de Saint Étienne du Mont, Paris*, lithograph, 1924, 15¹/₂ x 10¹/₄, edition of 100.

219. *Porte Saint Martin, Paris,* lithograph, 1924, 8³/₄ x 7⁷/₈, edition of 100.

220. *Rue de l'Abbaye, Paris*, lithograph, 1924, 14⅝ x 9, edition of 100.

221. *Rue de la Bûcherie, Paris,* lithograph, 1924, 10³/₄ x 12, edition of 100.

222. *Rue du Dragon, Paris*, lithograph, 1924, 9 x 13, edition of 100.

RUE FREDERIC-SAUTON
PARIS - 1924

223. *Rue Frédéric-Sauton, Paris,* lithograph, 1924, 12³/₄ x 9¹/₄, edition of 100.

RUE DE LA MONTAGNE - STE - GENEVIÈVE
PARIS 1924

224. *Rue de la Montagne Sainte Geneviève, Paris,* lithograph, 1924, 15³/₄ x 10, edition of 100.

225. *Rue Saint Séverin, Paris,* lithograph, 1924, 15³/₄ x 10, edition of 100.

226. *Saint Nicolas-des-Champs, Paris,* lithograph, 1924, 14 x 8³/₄, edition of 100.

LE VASE DU PANTHEON
PARIS
1924

SLC

227. *Le Vase du Panthéon, Paris*, lithograph, 1924, 14½ x 10½, edition of 100.

Within the illustration:

MAISON Vᵉ MELINE

COMMERCE

VIELLE MAISON
RUE ST. ETIENNE DU MONT   PARIS
1924

228. *Vieille Maison, Rue Saint Étienne du Mont, Paris*, lithograph, 1924, 14¼ x 11, edition of 100.

NOS. 229–240

The following twelve entries describe prints published as the portfolio Twelve Etchings of Yale.

229. *Davenport College*, drypoint, November 1933, 9⁹/₁₆ x 9⁷/₈, edition of 125.

230. *Divinity School Quadrangle*, drypoint, November 1933, 6¹/₂ x 9³/₄, edition of 125.

231. *Harkness Memorial Tower*, drypoint, November 1933, 13⁹/₁₆ x 9¹⁵/₁₆, edition of 125.

232. *Sheffield Scientific School Tower*, drypoint, November 1933, 10¹/₂ x 7⁵/₈, edition of 125.

233. *Graduate School*, drypoint, March 1934, $11^{1}/_{2}$ x $7^{7}/_{8}$, edition of 125.

234. *Calhoun College*, drypoint, August 1934, 8¹/₈ x 9⁷/₈, edition of 125.

235. *Jonathan Edwards College*, drypoint, August 1934, 11⁹/₁₆ x 7¹/₁₆, edition of 125.

236. *Sterling Law Buildings*, drypoint, August 1934, $8^{15}/_{16}$ x $11^5/_8$, edition of 125.

237. *University Library Entrance Portal*, drypoint, August 1934, 10⁹/₁₆ x 7⁵/₈, edition of 125.

238. *Bingham Hall and Hale Statue*, drypoint, October 1934, 11⁷/₈ x 8¹/₄, edition of 125.

239. *Payne Whitney Gymnasium*, drypoint, October 1934, 12 x 8¹/₂, edition of 125.

240. *Pierson College*, drypoint, October 1934, 10⅛ x 6⅞, edition of 125.

NOS. 241–249

The following nine entries describe drypoints engraved during 1935 and 1936 for use as covers of the periodical Pencil Points.

241. *Boston Courtyard*, drypoint, c. summer 1935, 6 x 3⅛, a few proofs. The print has been reproduced over the title *Old Court, Philadelphia*.

242. *Mission Courtyard, San Juan Capistrano, California*, drypoint, c. summer 1935, 5¹⁵⁄₁₆ x 3¹⁄₁₆, a few proofs.

243.
Apse of the Cathedral of Saint John the Divine, New York,
drypoint, c. summer 1935, 6 x 3¹⁄₈, a few proofs.

244. *The Derelicts, Rockland, Maine*, drypoint,
c. autumn 1935, 5⁷⁄₈ x 3¹⁄₁₆, a few proofs.

245. *Central Park, New York*, drypoint,
c. autumn 1935, 6 x 3⅛, a few proofs.

246. *Concord in Winter*, drypoint, c. autumn 1935,
6 x 3⅛, a few proofs. The print also is known by
the title *Winter, Concord, Massachusetts*.

247. *The "Scotch" Boardman House, Saugus, Massachusetts,* drypoint, c. autumn 1935, $3^7/_{16}$ x $3^7/_8$, a few proofs.

248.
Fisherman's Shanty, Marblehead, drypoint,
c. winter 1936, 4⅛ x 4⅝, a few proofs.

249. *Soviet Housing Development*, drypoint,
winter 1936, 4⅝ x 5, a few proofs.
This print also is known by the title
Cité de la Muette, Drancy.

NOS. 250–257

*The following eight entries describe prints
engraved to illustrate books or portfolios.*

250. *A Gateway in Toledo*, etching, 1926, 6 x 4, a few proofs.

251. *A Study of Trees*, drypoint, 1926, 5 x 7, edition of 255, as well as a few working proofs and about 15 artist's proofs. The subject is imaginary.

252. *The City Cross, Winchester*, etching, 1928, $9^5/_{16}$ x $6^1/_2$, more than 3000 proofs.
The print also is known by the title *Butter Cross, Winchester*.

253. *The Market Place, Bourges*, etching, 1928, 6³/₄ x 5³/₈, edition of more than 3000.

254. *Street Scene, Woebley*, drypoint, c. 1928, 4⁷/₈ x 6³/₄, about 9 proofs, including 2 working proofs.

255. *A Windmill*, drypoint, c. 1928, 10⁷/₈ x 7, edition of 50. The setting of the subject is Essex, England.

256. *General Washington Saying Farewell to His Officers in Fraunces Tavern, New York,*
etching, 1932, 6¹/₄ x 8¹/₂, edition of 1000, as well as a few artist's proofs.

257. *Butcher Row, Coventry*, drypoint, 1941, $7^3/8$ x $5^7/8$, edition of 300, as well as 2 working proofs.

NOS. 258–269

The following twelve entries describe prints engraved to illustrate two special editions of the autobiography The Education of Henry Adams.

258. *The Adams Mansion, Quincy,* dry-wiped etching, c. 1940,
6⁷/₈ x 4⁵/₈, edition of 1500, as well as a few working proofs.

259. *The Harvard Yard, Cambridge,* second state.

259. *The Harvard Yard, Cambridge,* dry-wiped etching, c. 1940,
6⅞ x 4⅝, edition of 1500, as well as a few working proofs.
The plate has been cut down at bottom.

260. *The Houses of Parliament, London*, dry-wiped etching, c. 1940, $6^7/8$ x $4^5/8$, edition of 1500.

261. *Mont-Saint-Michel*, dry-wiped etching, c. 1940, 6⁷/₈ x 4⁵/₈, edition of 1500.

262. *Mount Vernon Street, Boston*, dry-wiped etching, c. 1940,
6⁷/₈ x 4⁵/₈, edition of 1500, as well as a few working proofs.

263. *The North Porch of the Virgin of Chartres, a Vista,*
dry-wiped etching, c. 1940, 6⁷/₈ x 4⁵/₈, edition of 1500,
as well as a few working proofs.

264. *The Steps of Ara Coeli, Rome*, dry-wiped etching, c. 1940,
6⁷/₈ x 4⁵/₈, edition of 1500.

265. *The Town of Chartres*, dry-wiped etching, c. 1940, 6⁷/₈ x 4⁵/₈, edition of 1500, as well as 4 working proofs.

266. *The Transept of the Cathedral of Notre Dame, Paris*,
dry-wiped etching, c. 1940, 6⁷/₈ x 4⁵/₈, edition of 1500.

267. *The Wadsworth House, Cambridge,* dry-wiped etching,
c. 1940, 6⁷/₈ x 4⁵/₈, edition of 1500.

268. *Wenlock Abbey, Shropshire*, dry-wiped etching,
c. 1940, 6⁷/₈ x 4⁵/₈, edition of 1500.

269. *Winter Evening on Beacon Street, Boston*, dry-wiped etching, c. 1940, 6⁷/₈ x 4⁵/₈, edition of 1500.

NOS. 270–282

*The following thirteen entries describe plates engraved
for print clubs and those commissioned by other organizations, as well as one donated edition.*

270. *The Tontine Crescent, Franklin Place, Boston*, drypoint, 1928, 6³/₄ x 5³/₈,
edition of 100. The print also is known by the titles *The Boston Library Plate*
and *The Club of Odd Volumes Plate*.

271. *Hospital Santa Cruz, Toledo*, drypoint, c. 1934, 9³/₁₆ x 7⁵/₈, edition of 300, as well as a single working proof, printed from the untrimmed plate, 10 x 8¹/₂.

272. *Mediterranean Village, Villefranche-sur-Mer*, drypoint, 1938, 8⁷/₁₆ x 11³/₄, about 300 proofs, including a single working proof. The print also is known by the title *The Harbor, Villefranche-sur-Mer*.

273. *Early Morning Market, Senlis*, drypoint, 1939, 9¹/₈ x 6³/₄, edition of 300, as well as a few working proofs.

274. *The King Hooper Mansion*, etching, 1939, 7³/₄ x 5¹³/₁₆. A few
artist's proofs were printed upon completion of the plate. In 1953, an
edition of 300 was printed. The subject is located in Marblehead,
Massachusetts. The above title also has been used mistakenly to identify
two other prints: No. 201, *Hooper Street*, and No. 275, *Summer Shadows*.

275. *Summer Shadows*, drypoint, 1940, 8⁵/₈ x 11¹/₈, edition of 300, as well as
a few working proofs. The subject is a view of Bank Square, Marblehead.
The print also is known by the title *The King Hooper Mansion*.

276. *Harbor Side, Friendship, Maine*, drypoint, 1946, 8¹¹/₁₆ x 12¹¹/₁₆, edition of 300, as well as 16 working proofs.

277. *Old Nassau Hall, Princeton*, drypoint, 1946, 11³/₈ x 8¹/₈, edition of 300.

278. *Doorway of the Harvard Club, Boston*, drypoint, c. 1948, 8¹¹/₁₆ x 5⅝, edition of 100. The print also is known by the title *The Front Door*.

279. *Harvard Hall*, drypoint, c. 1948, 9⅝ x 8, edition of 100, as well as about 3 working proofs.
The setting of the subject is the Harvard Club, Boston, Massachusetts.
The print also is known by the title *The Great Hall*.

280. *Jacquemart, Moulins*, drypoint, 1948, 13⁵/₈ x 8¹¹/₁₆, edition of 100, as well as 4 working proofs.

281. *Barnegat Cottage, Marblehead*, drypoint, 1949, 8^1/$_{16}$ x 11^1/$_4$, edition of 300,
as well as 2 working proofs from the untrimmed plate, which measured 8^1/$_{16}$ x 12^1/$_4$.

282. *Saugus Ironworks*, drypoint, 1958, 7^1/$_8$ x 11^1/$_8$, edition of 300, as well as 3 working proofs.

NOS. 283–286

The following four entries comprise a group of privately commissioned plates.

283. *Continental Illinois Bank and Trust Company*, drypoint, c. 1935, 14³/₈ x 11¹¹/₁₆, edition of 100, as well as a few working proofs. The subject is located in Chicago, Illinois.

284. *Bank of New York and Trust Company*, drypoint, c. 1936, 10½ x 5½, about 10 proofs. The subject is located in New York City.

285. *Memorial Chapel*, drypoint, c. 1949, 6½ x 11, edition of 50, as well as a few artist's proofs.
The subject of the print is the Duncan Memorial Chapel, Floydsburg, Kentucky.

286. *First National Bank Building of Boston*, drypoint, 1949, 10³/₁₆ X 9⁵/₈,
about 16 proofs, including 6 working proofs.

APPENDICES

APPENDIX I
Unfinished Plates

A. Untitled (view of Amalfi from the waterfront), planned for drypoint, c. 1936, 12¼ x 8¼, no known proofs.

The upper middle portion of the plate is engraved in detail. The remainder of the design is engraved only in outline. The plate was found in the artist's studio after his death.

B. Untitled (scene of a riverbank, with boats in the foreground, buildings in the middle ground, a large tree on the left-hand side of the plate, and smaller trees in the background), planned for drypoint, c. 1938, 3 x 5, no known proofs.

The subject is probably a French scene. The design is engraved on the plate only lightly in outline. The plate was found in the artist's studio after his death.

C. Untitled (scene of a riverbank with shrubs in the left foreground, houses on the opposite bank on the right-hand side of the plate, and trees in the center middle ground), planned for drypoint, c. 1938, 3 x 5, no known proofs.

The subject is probably a French scene. The design is engraved on the plate only lightly in outline. The plate was found in the artist's studio after his death.

D. Untitled (view of Chartres, showing the lower town with the cathedral indicated in the background), planned for etching, c. 1940, 7¼ x 5¼, no known proofs.

The design is drawn lightly on the etching ground over the entire plate. Only a small portion on the right-hand side of the plate is engraved in detail. The plate is a version of the design for No. 265, *The Town of Chartres*. The plate was found in the artist's studio after his death.

E. Untitled (view of Mont-Saint-Michel, a horizontal design), planned for etching, c. 1940, 5¼ x 7¼, no known proofs.

The design is drawn lightly on the etching ground. Only a small portion of the plate is engraved in detail. The artist discarded the plate in favor of a vertical design of the same subject, No. 261, *Mont-Saint-Michel*. The plate was found in the artist's studio after his death.

F. Untitled (view of the schooner *Reine Marie Stuart*, docked in a cove near Thomaston, Maine), planned for drypoint, c. 1940, 8⅞ x 12½, no known proofs.

A horizontal design of the ship and surrounding waterfront is engraved lightly in outline on the plate. Only the upper left-hand quarter has been engraved in detail. The subject is derived from one of the artist's photographs. The plate was found in the artist's studio after his death.

G. Untitled (view of the Wren Building, College of William and Mary, Williamsburg, Virginia), drypoint, c. 1947, 8¾ x 11¹³/₁₆, no known proofs.

The plate was found in the artist's studio after his death and is of the same subject and similar design as print No. 142, *The Wren Building, Williamsburg*.

H. Untitled (interior resembling an antique shop), planned for drypoint, c. 1948, 7 x 10⅛, no known proofs.

The design is engraved very lightly in outline on the entire plate. The setting of the subject is not known. The plate was found in the artist's studio after his death.

I. *Saint Patrick's Cathedral, New York*, planned for drypoint, c. 1948, 14³/₁₆ x 10³/₁₆, no known proofs.

A vertical design of the front of the cathedral and surrounding skyscrapers is engraved lightly in outline on the entire plate. The plate was found in the artist's studio after his death.

APPENDIX II

Notes on Printing and Publishing

1. *A Side Street in Beauvais*
The working proofs are inscribed respectively "1ˢᵗ· state" and "1ⁱᵉʳ· état." The print was reproduced in the periodical *The American Architect*, August 12, 1925, plate 216. This etching is the first one published by the artist.

2. *Notre Dame from the Quai de l'Hôtel de Ville*
The print was reproduced to illustrate an article written by the artist and published in the periodical *The American Architect*, August 12, 1925, page 119.

3. *The Blacksmith's Shop, Senlis*
The edition is printed on various papers. The proposed edition of one hundred proofs was limited to twenty-two on November 1, 1928. The print was reproduced to illustrate an article written by the artist and published in the periodical *The American Architect*, August 12, 1925, page 122.

4. *Old Houses in Rouen*
The edition was limited to thirteen proofs on November 1, 1928. At a later date, proof number 8 was destroyed.

5. *The Loggia di Lanzi, Florence*
The edition was limited to thirty-three proofs on November 1, 1928, and proof number 16 was destroyed. The print was reproduced on the cover of the periodical *The Architectural Record* in 1925.

6. *Taormina*
The edition was limited to twenty proofs on November 1, 1928. The print was reproduced on the cover of the periodical *The Architectural Record* in 1925.

7. *Buttresses of Beauvais Cathedral*
The print was reproduced in the periodical *The American Architect*, August 12, 1925, plate 212.

8. *Amalfi*
The single working proof is inscribed "First State." A few proofs are printed contre-collé on Japan paper. The original sketch for the print is at the Cleveland School of Art, Cleveland, Ohio. The print was reproduced in the periodical *The American Architect*, August 12, 1925, plate 215.

9. *The Curiosity Shop, Rue Campagne Première, Paris*
The proposed edition of one hundred proofs was limited to thirteen on November 1, 1928. The print was reproduced to illustrate an article written by the artist and published in the periodical *The American Architect*, August 12, 1925, page 120.

10. *Church of San Giovanni Battiste, Siracusa*
The proposed edition of one hundred proofs was limited to thirty-six on November 1, 1928. The print was reproduced to illustrate an article written by the artist and published in the periodical *The American Architect*, August 12, 1925, page 120.

11. *Church of Saint Ayoul, Provins*

The edition was limited to sixty-eight proofs on November 1, 1928. A pencil drawing with the same title and subject and of similar design was reproduced to illustrate an article written by the artist and published in the periodical *The American Architect*, May 21, 1924.

12. *The Church at Sézanne*

A drawing of the same subject and similar design was reproduced in the periodical *Journal of the American Institute of Architects* about 1925.

13. *Semur-en-Auxois*

One of two working proofs is inscribed "First state" at the left-hand lower edge of the paper. The edition was limited to thirty-two proofs on November 1, 1928. At a later date, proof number 24 was destroyed. A drawing of the same subject and similar design was reproduced in the periodical *Arts and Decoration* about 1925.

14. *A Gateway in Seville*

One of three working proofs is inscribed "First state" at the lower edge of the paper. The proposed edition of one hundred proofs was limited to thirty-five at a later date. A drawing of the same subject and similar design was reproduced in the periodical *Century* during 1925.

15. *Gateway of Santa Maria, Burgos*

The single working proof is inscribed "First state" at the lower edge of the paper. The proposed edition of one hundred proofs was limited to thirty-five on November 1, 1928. A drawing of the same subject and similar design was reproduced in the periodical *Century* about 1925.

16. *House on the River, Albi*

The edition was limited to twenty on November 1, 1928. Proof number 11 was destroyed. A drawing of the same subject and similar design was reproduced in the periodical *The Architectural Record* about 1925.

17. *Old Houses in Lisieux*

The proposed edition of one hundred proofs was limited to twenty-eight on November 1, 1928. The print was reproduced to illustrate an article written by the artist and published in the periodical *The American Architect*, August 12, 1925, page 121.

18. *The Cypresses, Siracusa*

The proposed edition of one hundred proofs was limited to sixty-one on November 1, 1928. Proof number 31 was destroyed. The print was reproduced in the periodical *The American Architect*, August 12, 1925, plate 213.

19. *The Giant Buttress, Bourges*

One of two working proofs is inscribed "Trial proof." The proposed edition of one hundred proofs was limited to fourteen on November 1, 1928. Two proofs, numbers 9 and 10, were destroyed. A drawing of the same subject and similar design was reproduced in the periodical *Journal of the American Institute of Architects* during 1926.

20. *The Fish Market, Chartres*

Of the proposed edition of one hundred proofs, only seventy were printed. Twenty-one proofs were destroyed, and the edition was limited to forty-nine on November 1, 1928.

21. *Springtime in Senlis*

Two of three working proofs are inscribed respectively "First state" and "Second state." Some proofs are printed in brown ink. The plate, which was engraved directly from nature, was destroyed in the summer of 1927. The print was reproduced in the periodical *The American Architect*, August 12, 1925, plate 217.

22. *Rue Daubenton, Paris*

The plate was destroyed in the summer of 1927. The print was reproduced in the periodical *The American Architect*, August 12, 1925, plate 214, and in the book *Through France With a Sketchbook*, page 101.

23. *The Bridge of Pinos, Spain*

The plate was destroyed in the summer of 1927. This drypoint is the first one published by the artist. A pen and ink drawing with the same title and subject and of similar design was reproduced to illustrate an article written by the artist and published in the periodical *The American Architect*, July 16, 1924, page 43.

24. *The Beach, Minori*
The plate was destroyed in the summer of 1927.

25. *Rue Mouffetard, Paris*
The edition is printed in sepia ink on Chinese paper.

26. *The Cloister, Saint Benoît*
The proofs are printed in sepia or black ink on Chinese paper. The proposed edition of thirty proofs supposedly was limited to thirteen on November 1, 1928. The artist's records also show that at least ten proofs have been sold over the years. However, fifteen proofs were found in the artist's studio after his death.

27. *The Tower in Andujar*
Of the proposed edition of thirty-five proofs, twenty-five were printed, all in sepia ink.

28. *Châteaudun*
Of the proposed edition of thirty proofs, twenty-six were printed. Some, if not all, are printed in sepia ink. A drawing with the same title and subject and of similar design was reproduced in the periodical *American Architect and Architecture* during 1925.

29. *The Chateau in the Lot*
The edition is printed on Chinese paper in sepia ink.

30. *Gateway in Perpignan*
All proofs are printed in sepia ink. The print was reproduced in the periodical *The American Architect*, September 9, 1925, plate 240.

33. *The Poplars*
Of the proposed edition of twenty-five proofs, about eighteen were printed.

34. *An Alley in Pont Audemer*
Of the proposed edition of fifteen proofs, about eight were printed. "Not considered published" is the artist's notation in his records about this print.

35. *Vitré*
The plate has been canceled. Its whereabouts is unknown. The print was reproduced to illustrate an article written by the artist and published in the periodical *The American Architect*, December 5, 1926, page 430.

38. *The Porches, Dinan*
The plate has been canceled. Its whereabouts is unknown. The print was reproduced over the title *Old Houses, Dinan*, in the periodical *The American Architect*, December 5, 1926.

39. *Remnants of Gothic Lace Work, Pont Audemer*
A second state of a single proof is noted in the artist's records. No records of other states have been found. The plate has been canceled. Its whereabouts is unknown.

40. *The Valley in Vitré*
A few artist's proofs as well as the catalogue proof are printed contre-collé. "Never published" is the artist's notation in his records about the print. The print was reproduced to illustrate an article written by the artist and published in the periodical *The American Architect*, December 5, 1926, page 431.

41. *Pont Audemer*
Some proofs are printed contre-collé. "Never published" is the artist's notation in his records about the print.

42. *Vieilles Maisons, Dinan*
The edition is printed on Chinese, white, and buff papers in black or bistre ink.

43. *The Farm Gate, Vernonnet*
Proofs are printed in black or bistre ink on white, Chinese, or cream papers. Some proofs are printed contre-collé. Of the proposed edition of thirty proofs, twenty-five were printed; and of those, fourteen were destroyed. "Not considered published" is the artist's notation in his records about the print.

44. *The Spires of Coutances*
Proofs are printed in black or bistre ink on white or Chinese papers. Some proofs are printed

contre-collé. Of the proposed edition of thirty-five proofs, twenty-seven were printed; and of those, sixteen were destroyed. "Not considered published" is the artist's notation in his records about the print.

45. *The Village Church, Menilles*
The plate has been canceled. Its whereabouts is unknown.

46. *The Quais, Saint Tropez*
The artist's records note a first state of three proofs.

47. *The Hilltop, Villefranche-sur-Mer*
A first state of three proofs is noted in the artist's records.

48. *The Waterfront, Villefranche-sur-Mer*
A first state of three proofs is noted in the artist's records.

49. *The Battered Boat, Villefranche-sur-Mer*
A first state of three proofs is noted in the artist's records. A brush and ink drawing of the same subject and similar design was reproduced to illustrate an article written by the artist and published in the periodical *The American Architect*, April 20, 1927, page 493.

50. *Old Menton*
A first state of three proofs is noted in the artist's records. Proofs are printed on cream or Ingres papers. The plate has been canceled. Its whereabouts is unknown. The print was reproduced over the title *Menton Gateway* in the periodical *The American Architect*, May 20, 1927, page 634, and over the title *A Menton Gateway* in the book *Through France With a Sketchbook*.

51. *The Sheltered Street, Vitré*
Proofs are printed on various papers. Of the edition of thirty-five proofs, twenty were destroyed on November 1, 1928. The print was reproduced over the title *The Porches, Vitré* to illustrate an article written by the artist and published in the periodical *The American Architect*, December 15, 1926, page 431.

52. *Petite Venise, Colmar*
A working proof with pencil-drawn shading

has been reproduced over the title *Little Venice* to illustrate an article written by the artist and published in the periodical *The American Architect*, July 20, 1927, page 71.

53. *Broom Shop, Lucca*
The edition is printed on various papers. Some proofs are printed contre-collé.

54. *Cathedral Spires, Angers*
The edition is printed on antique paper and Ingres paper. A ". . . unique first state before trimming of the plate" is noted in the artist's records. Neither the dimensions of the plate before trimming nor of the single first proof are known.

55. *The Veterans, Josselin*
The edition is printed on Ingres paper and "papier ancien." The print was reproduced to illustrate an article written by the artist and published in the periodical *The American Architect*, February 20, 1928, page 211.

56. *Fishing Boats, Menton*
Proofs are printed on Chinese paper in sepia or black ink. Some proofs are printed contre-collé. Twenty-six proofs were printed of the proposed edition of fifty. Seventeen proofs were destroyed on November 1, 1928. "Not considered published" is the artist's notation in his records about the print. The print was reproduced over the above title in the monograph *Samuel Chamberlain, Etcher and Lithographer*, by Charles D. Childs, published by Charles Goodspeed and Company, Boston, 1927. The print was reproduced over the title *The Harbor, Menton* in the periodical *The American Architect*, May 20, 1927, page 269, and in the book *Through France With a Sketchbook*, page 66.

57. *Menton Tenements*
Proofs are printed in black or bistre ink on Chinese paper. Some proofs are printed contre-collé. Of the edition of fifty proofs, thirty-four were destroyed on November 1, 1928. "Not published" is the artist's notation in his records about the print.

58. *Colmar*
Proofs are printed on Chinese or Japan papers. Some proofs are printed contre-collé. Of the edition

of fifty proofs, thirty-nine were destroyed on November 1, 1928. "Not considered published" is the artist's notation in his records about the print. The print was reproduced over the title *The Market-Place, Colmar*, in the periodical *The American Architect*, July 1927, page 75.

59: *Porte du Vieux Pont, Sospel*
Many proofs are printed on Japan paper.

60. *Siena*
The edition is printed on "papier ancien verdâtre."

61. *Tunis*
The proposed edition of one hundred proofs was not printed. Only working proofs and a few artist's proofs were printed. "Edition withdrawn, never published" is the artist's notation about the print in his records. The print is the artist's only aquatint executed in color. A pencil and wash drawing with the same title and subject and of similar design was reproduced to illustrate an article written by the artist and published in the periodical *The American Architect*, June 3, 1925, page 489.

62. *Gables of Colmar*
Each of three working proofs is inscribed "First state." The edition is printed on "papier ancien" and Canson new paper.

63. *Plaza de San Martin, Segovia*
A first state of a single proof exists. Some proofs are printed on "papier ancien."

64. *Perugia*
A first state of two proofs is noted in the artist's records. The edition is printed on various papers. A pencil drawing with the same title and subject and of similar design was reproduced to illustrate an article written by the artist and published in the periodical *The American Architect*, November 5, 1928, page 781.

66. *The Sunlit Tower, Colmar*
Four states of a single proof each are noted in the artist's records. The print was reproduced to illustrate an article written by the artist and pub-

lished in the periodical *The American Architect*, November 5, 1928. A pencil drawing with the same title and subject and of similar design was reproduced in the same issue of *The American Architect*.

68. *Broad Street, Ludlow*
The plate was engraved directly from nature. The edition was reserved for the Rembrandt Gallery of Robert Dunthorne and Son, London, England.

69. *Canterbury*
A first state of a single proof is noted in the artist's records. The plate was engraved directly from nature. The print was reproduced over the title *High Street, Canterbury*, as the frontispiece in the book *British Bouquet*.

70. *A Stable Court in Essex*
A first state of a single proof is noted in the artist's records. The plate was engraved directly from nature.

71. *Founders' Tower, Magdalen College, Oxford*
The plate was engraved directly from nature.

72. *An Umbrian Gateway*
Of the edition of fifty proofs, thirty-four were destroyed. The print was reproduced over the title *Gate near Orvieto* to illustrate an article written by the artist and published in the periodical *The American Architect*, March 20, 1928, page 354.

73. *Harness Shop*
The print was reproduced to illustrate an article written by the artist and published in the periodical *The American Architect*, February 20, 1928, page 213.

74. *Lucca*
A few proofs are printed contre-collé on Chinese or white papers. The print was reproduced to illustrate an article written by the artist and published in the periodical *The American Architect*, March 20, 1928, page 356.

75. *Salamanca Cathedral*
A first state of a single proof and four or five trial proofs are noted in the artist's records. The

edition is printed on antique paper and "papier verdâtre."

76. *Hôpital Saint Jean, Bruges*

A first state of a single proof, a second state of two proofs, and a third state of a single proof as well as a single trial proof are noted in the artist's records. The edition is printed on various papers, including antique paper and "papier verdâtre." A pencil drawing with the same title and subject and of similar design was reproduced to illustrate an article written by the artist and published in the periodical *The American Architect*, June 20, 1928, page 814.

77. *Far West Junk Shop*

Three states of a single proof each as well as a single trial proof are noted in the artist's records.

78. *Kansas City War Memorial*

Two states of a single proof each are noted in the artist's records. Of the edition of one hundred and twenty-five proofs, one hundred and eighteen were destroyed on January 3, 1930. The print was commissioned by Mr. J. H. Bender, publisher of *The Print Collector's Quarterly*, Alden Galleries, Kansas City, Missouri. The edition is noted in the artist's records as having been "Printed exclusively for Kansas City."

79. *Soaring Steel*

Two of four working proofs are inscribed respectively "Artist's proof—3rd. state" and "Artist's proof—4th. state." The remaining working proofs are not marked, and records of other states have not been found.

80. *Oil*

First and second states of a single proof each and a third state of two proofs are indicated in the artist's records. Of the edition of one hundred proofs, seventy-five were destroyed on January 3, 1930.

81. *Manhattan, Old and New*

First and second states of a single proof each and a third state of two proofs are noted in the artist's records. The title *New York, Ancien et Nouveau* is written on some prints in the artist's hand.

82. *Boston Fish Pier*

First and second states of a single proof each and a third state of two proofs are noted in the artist's records. The edition is printed on antique "papier verdâtre." The canceled plate, inscribed "To Charles D. Childs" and engraved with a spouting whale, is in the Wiggin Collection at the Boston Public Library, Boston, Massachusetts.

83. *Faneuil Hall, Boston*

First and second states of a single proof each and a third state of two proofs are noted in the artist's records. The edition is printed on antique "papier verdâtre." The plate, steel-faced and canceled with the inscription "To Matt B. Jones," is in the Wiggin Collection at the Boston Public Library, Boston, Massachusetts.

84. *Drizzly Morning in Chicago*

Some proofs are printed on antique paper. A first state of two proofs, printed on antique paper, is noted in the artist's records. The plate has been canceled by an inscription done in three lines from the top center to the top right of the plate. The inscription reads, "To Mrs. Bertha E. Jaques, with my good wishes, Samuel Chamberlain."

85. *The Customs Tower, Boston*

All proofs are printed on antique "papier verdâtre." A first state of two proofs is noted in the artist's records. Of the edition of one hundred proofs, ninety-three were destroyed on January 3, 1930. "Never published" is the artist's notation about the print in his records.

86. *The Curving Canyon, New York*

All proofs are printed on "papier verdâtre." A first state of two proofs is noted in the artist's records. Of the edition of one hundred proofs, forty were destroyed, probably during March 1935.

87. *Grain Elevators*

Many proofs are printed on white Rives paper. A first state of two proofs is noted in the artist's records. The edition was printed but never published.

88. *Verneuil*

Some proofs are printed on cream Rives paper. The artist's records note a first state of one proof, a second state of two proofs, and a third state of five proofs. The plate presumably was left in France and destroyed during World War II.

89. *La Charité-sur-Loire*

The artist's records note a first state of two proofs, a second state of a single proof, and a third state of four proofs. The edition is printed on various papers. The plate presumably was left in France and destroyed during World War II.

90. *Market Day in Lillebonne*

The artist's records note first and second states of a single proof each and third and fourth states of four proofs each. The plate presumably was left in France and destroyed during World War II.

91. *Auxerre*

The artist's records note first and second states of a single proof each and a third state of two proofs. The edition was reserved for the artist's Paris dealer, Marcel Guiot. The plate presumably was left in France and destroyed during World War II.

92. *Dentelles Gothiques, Clamecy*

The artist's records note first and second states of a single proof each and a third state of four proofs. The plate presumably was left in France and destroyed during World War II.

93. *Cathedral of Sens*

The artist's records note first and second states of a single proof each and a third state of three proofs. The plate presumably was left in France and destroyed during World War II.

94. *Skyscrapers of Menton*

Three states of a single proof each and a fourth state of two proofs as well as a trial proof are noted in the artist's records. The plate presumably was left in France and destroyed during World War II. A pencil drawing with the same title and subject and of similar design was reproduced to illustrate an article written by the artist and published in the periodical *The American Architect*, May 20, 1927, page 631.

95. *Towers of Senlis*

All proofs are printed on eighteenth-century French paper. Three states of a single proof each and a fourth state of two proofs as well as two trial proofs are noted in the artist's records. The plate presumably was left in France and destroyed during World War II.

96. *Gateway in the Ghetto, Paris*

All proofs are printed on antique French paper. Four states of a single proof each as well as a single trial proof are noted in the artist's records. The print was used as the frontispiece of a deluxe edition of the book *France Will Live Again*, published in 1940. Each of fifty-five volumes contains a signed and numbered proof of the print. The plate presumably was left in France and destroyed during World War II.

97. *Midsummer Silhouette*

Many proofs, if not all, are printed on white Rives paper. Three states of a single proof each and a fourth state of two proofs are noted in the artist's records. The plate presumably was left in France and destroyed during World War II.

98. *The Shadowy Street*

First and second states of a single proof each and a third state of two proofs are noted in the artist's records. Fifty proofs of the edition of seventy-five are printed on bleached nineteenth-century French paper. The plate presumably was left in France and destroyed during World War II.

99. *Fruit Store Façade*

The artist's records indicate first and third states of a single proof each and a second state of two proofs as well as a few trial proofs. The first fifty proofs of the edition are printed on eighteenth-century ledger paper. The plate presumably was left in France and destroyed during World War II.

100. *Place Notre Dame, Senlis*

Three states of a single proof each as well as a single trial proof are noted in the artist's records. Fifty proofs of the edition of seventy-five are printed on thin white Rives paper. The plate presumably was left in France and destroyed during World War II.

101. *The Mason's House, Senlis*

The artist's records note a first state of two proofs and second and third states of a single proof each. The plate presumably was left in France and destroyed during World War II.

102. *Slums of Rouen*

The artist's records note first and second states of two proofs each, a third state of seventeen proofs, a fourth state of eighteen proofs, and a fifth state of a single proof. The proposed edition of one hundred proofs was not printed. "Never published" is the artist's notation about the print in his records. The plate presumably was left in France and destroyed during World War II.

103. *Porte Saint Guillaume, Chartres*

The artist's records note three states of a single proof each. The plate presumably was left in France and destroyed during World War II.

104. *Chartres Cathedral*

Three states of a single proof each are noted in the artist's records. The edition is printed on Chinese paper. The plate presumably was left in France and destroyed during World War II.

105. *Beauvais*

The artist's records indicate two states of a single proof each and a third state of either two or five proofs. The plate presumably was left in France and destroyed during World War II.

106. *Silhouette of Senlis*

The artist's records note a first state of a single proof and second and third states of two proofs. The plate presumably was left in France and destroyed during World War II.

107. *The Verdant Village*

A first state of a single proof, a second state of two proofs, and a third state of three proofs are noted in the artist's records. Forty proofs of the edition of one hundred are printed on antique paper. The plate, engraved directly from nature, presumbly was left in France and destroyed during World War II.

108. *The Saplings*

First and second states of a single proof each and a third state of two proofs are noted in the artist's records. The edition is printed on antique paper. The plate, engraved directly from nature, presumably was left in France and destroyed during World War II.

109. *The Abbey Farm*

The artist's records note a first state of a single proof and a second state of two proofs. The plate, engraved directly from nature, presumably was left in France and destroyed during World War II.

110. *Senlis from a Crow's Nest*

First and second states of a single proof each and a third state of two proofs are noted in the artist's records. The title *Senlis from a Bird's Nest* is written on some proofs in the artist's hand. The plate presumably was left in France and destroyed during World War II.

111. *Manhattan Twilight*

The working proofs are noted in the artist's records as follows: a first state of two proofs, a second state of a single proof, a third state of two proofs, fourth and fifth states of a single proof each, sixth and seventh states of two proofs each, an eighth state of a single proof, and a ninth state of two proofs. The plate presumably was left in France and destroyed during World War II.

112. *Espalion*

The artist's records note first and third states of a single proof each, as well as five trial proofs. No records of other states have been found. The plate was found in the artist's studio after his death.

113. *Lisieux*

The artist's records note three states of a single proof each, as well as five trial proofs. Two of these are inscribed respectively "Final state—2/2" and "Artist's proof—final state." The edition was printed in London for Rembrandt Galleries of Robert Dunthorne and Son, London, England. The plate was found in the artist's studio after his death.

114. *Albi Sunset*

The artist's records note first and second states of a single proof each and a third state of five proofs.

115. *The Country Road*

The artist's records note three states of a single proof each. The plate, which had been engraved directly from nature, was found in the artist's studio after his death.

116. *The Abandoned Chateau*

A first state of a single proof, second and third states of two proofs each, and a fourth state of five proofs are noted in the artist's records. The artist further engraved the plate on February 21, 1940, to demonstrate the process of drypoint to a gathering of friends and members of the Club of Odd Volumes in Boston, Massachusetts. The first proof printed from the reworked plate was given to Professor George Lyman Kittredge of Harvard University, Cambridge, Massachusetts. Professor Kittredge was present at this demonstration. The plate was found in the artist's studio after his death.

117. *The Abbey of Montmajour*

The artist's records note two states of a single proof each. Some proofs of the edition were printed in France by Edmond Rigal. The remaining proofs were printed in Boston, Massachusetts. The plate was found in the artist's studio after his death.

118. *Quimper*

The artist's records note first and second states of a single proof each and third and fourth states of three proofs each, as well as a single trial proof. The plate was found in the artist's studio after his death.

119. *The Giant Oak*

The artist's records note a first state of three proofs. The plate was found in the artist's studio after his death.

120. *Burgundy Hillside*

The artist's records note a second state of two proofs. No records of other states have been found. The plate was found in the artist's studio after his death.

121. *Essex Village*

The artist's records note two states of a single proof each. The plate was found in the artist's studio after his death.

122. *Noon in Noyers*

The artist's records note first and second states of two proofs each and third and fourth states of a single proof each. The plate was found in the artist's studio after his death.

123. *Summer Street, Marblehead*

The artist's records note two states of two proofs each. The plate was found in the artist's studio after his death. The print was reproduced, and an edition of three hundred copies was printed by The Meriden Gravure Company, Meriden, Connecticut. This edition was copyrighted in 1972 and sold by The Marblehead Arts Association of Marblehead, Massachusetts. The reproduced edition has the same dimensions as the original print but is named *Summer Shadows*. The drypoint titled *Summer Shadows* is described in entry No. 275.

124. *Stonington Sunset*

The artist's records note a first state of a single proof and second and third states of two proofs each, as well as five trial proofs. The plate was found in the artist's studio after his death.

125. *Saunderstown Fields*

The artist's records note three states of a single proof each and a fourth state of two proofs. The plate was found in the artist's studio after his death.

126. *Sunshine After Showers, the "Nantucket"*

The artist's records note a first state of one proof, a second state of two proofs, and third and fourth states of a single proof each, as well as four proofs listed as "Trial artist's proofs." The plate was found in the artist's studio after his death.

127. *Springtime in Salem*

The artist's records note four states of a single proof each and five "Trial artist's proofs." The plate was found in the artist's studio after his death. The print was reproduced, and an edition of three hundred copies was printed by The Meriden Gravure

Company, Meriden, Connecticut. This edition of reproductions was copyrighted in 1974 by the Essex Institute of Salem, Massachusetts, and has the same title and dimensions as the original drypoint.

128. *The Rogers Building*

The artist's records note a first state of two proofs, a second state of a single proof, and five "Trial artist's proofs." At the time that the plate was engraved, the Rogers Building housed the School of Architecture of the Massachusetts Institute of Technology. The plate was found in the artist's studio after his death.

129. *Christ Church, Cambridge*

The artist's records note two states of a single proof each. The plate was found in the artist's studio after his death.

130. *Mediterranean Wash Day*

The artist's records note two states of a single proof each. The plate, which had been engraved directly from nature, was found in the artist's studio after his death.

131. *Bend in the Road*

The artist's records note three states of a single proof each and a fourth state of two proofs. The plate was found in the artist's studio after his death.

132. *Valley of the Var*

The artist's records note a first state of a single proof, a second state of two proofs, and third and fourth states of a single proof each, as well as a single trial proof. The plate was found in the artist's studio after his death.

133. *The Apothecary's Shop, Williamsburg*

The artist's records note three states of a single proof each, as well as a single trial proof. The steel-faced plate, which had been printed in France by Edmond Rigal, was found in the artist's studio after his death. The print was sold at the Craft House, Williamsburg, Virginia.

134. *The Capitol, Williamsburg*

The artist's records note three states of a single proof each, as well as a single trial proof. The steel-

faced plate, which had been printed in France by Edmond Rigal, was found in the artist's studio after his death. The print was sold at the Craft House, Williamsburg, Virginia.

135. *The Governor's Palace, Williamsburg*

The steel-faced plate, which had been printed in France by Edmond Rigal, was found in the artist's studio after his death. The print was sold at the Craft House, Williamsburg, Virginia.

136. *The Raleigh Tavern, Williamsburg*

The steel-faced plate, which had been printed in France by Edmond Rigal, was found in the artist's studio after his death. The print was sold at the Craft House, Williamsburg, Virginia.

137. *Bruton Parish Church, Williamsburg*

The artist's records note two states of a single proof each, as well as a single trial proof. The steel-faced plate, which had been printed in France by Edmond Rigal, was found in the artist's studio after his death. The print was sold at the Craft House, Williamsburg, Virginia.

138. *The Public Gaol, Williamsburg*

The artist's records note a first state of a single proof. The steel-faced plate, which had been printed in France by Edmond Rigal, was found in the artist's studio after his death. The print was sold at the Craft House, Williamsburg, Virginia.

139. *The Palace Gardens, Williamsburg*

The artist's records note a first state of a single proof. The steel-faced plate, which had been printed in France by Edmond Rigal, was found in the artist's studio after his death. The print was sold at the Craft House, Williamsburg, Virginia.

140. *Saint George Tucker House, Williamsburg*

Three states of a single proof each, a fourth state of two proofs, and fifth and sixth states of a single proof each were printed. The steel-faced plate, which had been printed in France by Edmond Rigal, was found in the artist's studio after his death. The print was sold at the Craft House, Williamsburg, Virginia.

141. *The Semple House, Williamsburg*

The artist's records note a first state of four proofs, a second state of two proofs, and third and fourth states of a single proof each. The steel-faced plate, which had been printed in France by Edmond Rigal, was found in the artist's studio after his death. The print was sold at the Craft House, Williamsburg, Virginia.

142. *The Wren Building, Williamsburg*

A second state of a single proof, a third state of five proofs, a fourth state of a single proof, and a fifth state of two proofs were printed. No records of the first state have been found, but an early proof is not marked. The plate was found in the artist's studio after his death. The untitled, unfinished plate described in entry "G" of the appendix "Unfinished Plates" is a similar design of the same subject.

143. *The Churchyard, Williamsburg*

The artist's records indicate three states of a single proof each, as well as a single trial proof. The steel-faced plate, which had been printed in France by Edmond Rigal, was found in the artist's studio after his death. The print was sold at the Craft House, Williamsburg, Virginia.

144. Untitled (landscape in the neighborhood of the colonial building Sign of the Golden Ball, Williamsburg, Virginia). The plate was found in the artist's studio after his death. The subject was identified by comparing the plate with photographs by the artist.

145. *An Alley in Pont Audemer*

The print was reproduced over the title *Courtyard in Beaune* to illustrate an article written by the artist and published in the periodical *The American Architect*, February 20, 1928, page 242.

146. *Modena, Italy*

The print was reproduced to illustrate an article written by the artist and published in the periodical *The American Architect*, March 20, 1928, page 351.

147. *Fontana Grande, Viterbo*

The print was reproduced to illustrate an article written by the artist and published in the periodical *The American Architect*, May 20, 1928, page 646.

148. *The Fountain, Viterbo*

The print was reproduced to illustrate an article written by the artist and published in the periodical *The American Architect*, May 20, 1928, page 643.

149. *Viterbo*

A pen and wash drawing with the same title and subject and of similar design was reproduced to illustrate an article written by the artist and published in the periodical *The American Architect*, May 20, 1928, page 645. The plate was found in the artist's studio after his death.

150. *Dijon*

The print was reproduced to illustrate an article written by the artist and published in the periodical *The American Architect*, September 9, 1925, page 209. The reproduction has the dimensions $3^1/_8$ x $3^1/_8$ and is the only known example of the print.

151. *The Plaza, Baza, Spain*

The print was reproduced to illustrate an article written by the artist and published in the periodical *The American Architect*, September 9, 1925, page 208. The reproduction has the dimensions $2^7/_{16}$ x $3^1/_8$ and is the only known example of the print.

152. *The Ponte Vecchio, Florence*

The print was reproduced to illustrate an article written by the artist and published in the periodical *The American Architect*, September 9, 1925, page 207. The reproduction has the dimensions $4^3/_4$ x $3^1/_8$ and is the only known example of the print.

153. *Street Scene, Angers*

The print was reproduced to illustrate an article written by the artist and published in the periodical *The American Architect*, October 20, 1927, page 495.

154. *Pietrasanta, Italy*

The print was reproduced to illustrate an article written by the artist and published in the periodical *The American Architect*, May 20, 1928, page 355.

155. *Pont Saint Bénézet, Avignon*

A pencil drawing with the same title and subject and of similar design was reproduced to illustrate an article written by the artist and published in the periodical *The American Architect*, September 24, 1924.

156. *The Square, Pont Audemer*

The print was reproduced over the title *Pont Audemer* to illustrate an article written by the artist and published in the periodical *The American Architect*, February 20, 1928, page 215.

157. *Vieux Saumur*

The print was reproduced over the above title to illustrate an article written by the artist and published in the periodical *The American Architect*, October 29, 1927, page 497. The print was reproduced over the title *Old Saumur* in the book *Through France with a Sketchbook*, page 37.

159. *A Chateau Farm near Siena*

A pencil drawing with the same title and subject and of similar design was reproduced to illustrate an article written by the artist and published in the periodical *The American Architect*, September 20, 1927, page 352.

160. *Château de Vitré*

Some proofs are printed in sepia ink. The print was reproduced over the above title in the periodical *The American Architect*, December 5, 1926, and over the title *The Chateau, Vitré*, in the book *Through France with a Sketchbook*, page 21.

161, 162, 163. *Farm Gate in the Oise*

A drawing of the same subject and similar design was reproduced over the title *Pigeonnier-Cousnicourt* in the book *France Will Live Again* at the lower left of page 148.

165, 166. *The Fortress, Carmona*

The above title is taken from inscriptions in the artist's hand on proofs of the prints. A proof of one print was reproduced over the title *Gate Way in Spain* in the artist's autobiography, *Etched in Sunlight*, page 26. On the same page, the artist referred to these plates as his "fledgling attempts at etching."

167. *The Market Place, Vernon*

The single artist's proof was reproduced as plate LII in the portfolio *Domestic Architecture in Rural France*.

168. *Tower of a Church, Angoulême*

A pen and ink drawing with the same title and subject and of similar design was reproduced to illustrate an article written by the artist and published in the periodical *The American Architect*, May 21, 1924, page 486.

169. *Town Gate, Rimini*

A pencil drawing with the same title and subject and of similar design was reproduced to illustrate an article written by the artist and published in the periodical *The American Architect*, March 20, 1928, page 354.

170. Untitled (French building with old gas pump).

The single known proof is inscribed "First state—only proof."

171. Untitled (French café and market, probably in Rouen). The single known proof is inscribed "Only first state."

178. *Ann Arbor*

All proofs are printed in sepia ink.

179. *Collegiate Sorosis House, Ann Arbor*

180. *Old Ann Arbor*

181. *Old House on Liberty Street, Ann Arbor*

182. *Phi Kappa Psi House, Ann Arbor*

183. Untitled (Ann Arbor scene of an old wooden bridge in a meadow)

Proofs from the above five plates are printed in sienna ink.

184. *Les Oliviers, Menton*

The artist referred to the print as "Never published" in a letter written to Charles D. Childs on December 4, 1927. The print was listed as "Out of print" in the monograph *Samuel Chamberlain, Etcher and Lithographer*, by Charles D. Childs, published by Charles E. Goodspeed and Company, Boston, 1927.

185. *Le Paysage Breton*

The print was reproduced to illustrate an article written by the artist and published in the periodical *The American Architect*, February 20, 1928.

186. *The Hilltop, Kersey*

A pencil drawing of the same subject and similar design was reproduced over the title *Kersey, Suffolk*, to illustrate the book *Tudor Homes of England*, page 23.

187. *Long Wittenham, Oxfordshire*

A pencil drawing with the same title and subject and of similar design was reproduced to illustrate the book *Tudor Homes of England*, page 231. The plate was found in the artist's studio after his death.

188. *Pembridge*

A pencil drawing with the same title and subject and of similar design was reproduced to illustrate the book *Tudor Homes of England*, page 139. Unfortunately, the print appears over the title *Pembroke* in the artist's autobiography, *Etched in Sunlight*, on page 180. A drypoint, No. 202, has the title *Pembroke*. The plate was found in the artist's studio after his death.

189. *Tewkesbury*

A pencil drawing with the same title and subject and of similar design was reproduced to illustrate the book *Tudor Homes of England*, page 139. The plate was found in the artist's studio after his death.

191. *Farm Vista, Le Plessis-Luzarches*

Two states of three proofs each were printed. The print was reproduced over the above title in the book *France Will Live Again*, page 143, and over the title *The Farm Gate* in the artist's autobiography, *Etched in Sunlight*, page 116. The plate presumably was left in France at the shop of Edmond Rigal and destroyed during World War II.

192. *Place de la Concorde, Paris*

The print was designed as a menu cover for a banquet held on July 30, 1931, by members of Les Bibliophiles de l'Automobile Club de France. The plate presumably was left in France at the shop of Edmond Rigal and destroyed during World War II.

193. *The Bridge at Sospel*

The print was reproduced to illustrate the book *France Will Live Again*, page 133. Print No. 59, *Porte du Vieux Pont, Sospel*, is a lithograph of the same subject and similar design. The plate presumably was left in France at the shop of Edmond Rigal and destroyed during World War II.

194. *College Saint Vincent, Senlis*

The plate presumably was left in France at the shop of Edmond Rigal and destroyed during World War II.

196. Untitled (houses along the quais, Paris).

The plate was found in the artist's studio after his death.

198. Untitled (scene of Amalfi from the harbor with an inscription on the right-hand side of the plate). The inscription, engraved from left to right, is as follows: "Plaque Commemorative à l'occasion de l'anniversaire nuptiale de MONSIEUR et MADAME William Emerson. Présentée par la Société Senlisienne Amicale et Fraternelle des ADMIRATEURS des EMERSONS." The plate was found in the artist's studio after his death.

199. *New England Hill Town*

Records exist of first and fourth states of three proofs each and a fifth state of a single proof, as well as a single trial proof. No records of other states have been found. An edition was not printed, because the artist considered the plate ruined by a scratch accidentally made after a few proofs had been printed. However, an early proof from the unscratched plate was reproduced by The Meriden Gravure Company, Meriden, Connecticut, and an edition of three hundred copies with the same title and dimensions as the original drypoint was printed. The edition of reproductions was copyrighted in 1975 by the Marblehead Historical Society, Marblehead, Massachusetts. Copies were sold for the benefit of the Marblehead Historical Society. The canceled plate was found in the artist's studio after his death.

200. *Lydia Pinkham Compound Label*

A broken oval floral border, engraved for the label of Lydia Pinkham's compound, was designed by the artist at the request of Charles Pinkham. A portrait of Lydia engraved by Arthur Heintzelman completed the label. See the artist's autobiography,

Etched in Sunlight, page 142. The plate was found in the artist's studio after his death.

201. *Hooper Street*

Proofs are printed in green, sepia, or sienna ink. The above title is written in the artist's hand on several proofs. The title *The King Hooper Mansion* is used to list the print in the artist's autobiography, *Etched in Sunlight*. The plate, which was found in the artist's studio after his death, had been engraved to demonstrate the process of soft-ground etching to a gathering at the King Hooper Mansion, Marblehead, Massachusetts, in June 1940, to celebrate Frank W. Benson's first twenty-five years as a print-maker. Frank Benson, Kerr Eby, Arthur Heintzelman, and Thomas Nason also were present on this occasion and demonstrated other printing processes. See *Etched in Sunlight*, pages 108–109. The title *Hooper Street* also was given to a reproduced edition of the drypoint No. 275, *Summer Shadows*. See entry No. 275 of this appendix.

202. *Pembroke*

The print depicts the same scene as an early etching, No. 188, *Pembridge*. The plate was engraved to demonstrate the technique of drypoint to a gathering at the New York World's Fair on June 25, 1940. "To Quincy P. Emery" is inscribed on the plate along with the artist's signature.

203. *East Hagebourne, Berkshire*

A pencil drawing with the same title and subject and of similar design was reproduced to illustrate the book *Tudor Homes of England*, page 219. The plate, which was found in the artist's studio after his death, had been engraved to demonstrate the process of drypoint to a gathering at the National Academy of Design, New York City, New York. The inscription on the plate, "To Caroline," honors a family friend, Caroline Hood Carlin.

212. *L'Épicerie, Rue Galande, Paris*

The print has been listed by the title *L'Épicerie, Rue Grande, Paris*, in the list of published prints appended to the artist's autobiography, *Etched in Sunlight*.

In 1924, the following twenty prints were printed by Gaston Dorfinant in Paris, France, and published by the artist as the portfolio *Vingts Lithographies du Vieux Paris*:

209. *Cour du Dragon, Paris*
210. *Le Dôme de l'Église du Val de Grâce, Paris*
211. *Échoppe d'Étameur, Paris*
212. *L'Épicerie, Rue Galande, Paris*
213. *Fontaine de la Grosse Horloge, Rouen*
214. *L'Horloge, Paris*
215. *La Maison du Saumon, Chartres*
216. *Maison de la Tourelle, Rue des Francs Bourgeois, Paris*
217. *Passy Ancien et Nouveau, Paris*
218. *Un Portail de l'Église de Saint Étienne du Mont, Paris*
219. *Porte Saint Martin, Paris*
220. *Rue de l'Abbaye, Paris*
221. *Rue de la Bûcherie, Paris*
222. *Rue du Dragon, Paris*
223. *Rue Frédéric-Sauton, Paris*
224. *Rue de la Montagne Sainte Geneviève, Paris*
225. *Rue Saint Séverin, Paris*
226. *Saint Nicolas-des-Champs, Paris*
227. *Le Vase du Panthéon, Paris*
228. *Veille Maison, Rue Saint Étienne du Mont, Paris*

The following twelve plates were printed on various papers, including Chinese, Japanese, and antique French, in France by Edmond Rigal. The plates presumably were left in Rigal's Paris studio and destroyed during World War II. The prints constitute the portfolio *Twelve Etchings of Yale*, published and copyrighted 1933, 1934 by the Yale University Press, New Haven, Connecticut. The copyrights were renewed by the artist in 1961, 1962. Pen and wash drawings of each collegiate subject were created by the artist to present the project to George Parmly Day, president of Yale University Press at that time. The drawings remained in the artist's estate.

229. *Davenport College*
230. *Divinity School Quadrangle*
231. *Harkness Memorial Tower*
232. *Sheffield Scientific School Tower*
233. *Graduate School*
234. *Calhoun College*

235. *Jonathan Edwards College*

236. *Sterling Law Buildings*

237. *University Library Entrance Portal*

238. *Bingham Hall and Hale Statue*

239. *Payne Whitney Gymnasium*

240. *Pierson College*

241. *Boston Courtyard*

The plate was engraved from a photograph by Maurice M. Feustmann. The print is listed by the above title in the appendix "Published Etchings, Drypoints and Lithographs, and Commissioned Prints" in the artist's autobiography, *Etched in Sunlight*. The print was reproduced with the title *Old Court, Philadelphia*, as the cover of the periodical *Pencil Points*, July 1935.

242. *Mission Courtyard, San Juan Capistrano, California*

The plate was engraved from a photograph by A. V. De Fonda. The print was reproduced on the cover of the periodical *Pencil Points*, August 1935.

243. *Apse of the Cathedral of Saint John the Divine, New York*

The print was reproduced on the cover of the periodical *Pencil Points*, September 1935.

244. *The Derelicts, Rockland, Maine*

The print was reproduced on the cover of the periodical *Pencil Points*, October 1935.

245. *Central Park, New York*

The print was reproduced on the cover of the periodical *Pencil Points*, November 1935.

246. *Concord in Winter*

The print is listed by the above title in the appendix of published prints in the artist's autobiography, *Etched in Sunlight*. The print was reproduced over the title *Winter, Concord, Massachusetts* for the cover of the periodical *Pencil Points*, December 1935.

247. *The "Scotch" Boardman House, Saugus, Massachusetts*

The print was reproduced on the cover of the periodical *Pencil Points*, January 1936.

248. *Fisherman's Shanty, Marblehead*

The print was reproduced on the cover of the periodical *Pencil Points*, February 1936.

249. *Soviet Housing Development*

The print is listed by the above title in the appendix "Published Etchings, Drypoints and Lithographs, and Commissioned Prints" in the artist's autobiography, *Etched in Sunlight*. The print was reproduced with the title *Cité de la Muette, Drancy* as the cover of the periodical *Pencil Points*, March 1936.

250. *A Gateway in Toledo*

The print was reproduced for the frontispiece of the publication *The Print Connoisseur*, April 1926.

251. *A Study of Trees*

The print was engraved for use as an example of the medium of drypoint to be included in the portfolio *The Graphic Processes: Intaglio, Relief, Planographic*, edited by Louis Holman and published by Goodspeed and Company, Boston, 1926. Each of two hundred and fifty-five portfolios contains a proof of the print.

252. *The City Cross, Winchester*

An edition of three thousand proofs was printed for inclusion as the frontispiece in the book *Tudor Homes of England*. Each volume contains a proof of the print. Some additional proofs, numbered as an edition of fifty, were printed on antique French ledger paper and were not bound in copies of the book.

253. *The Market Place, Bourges*

The edition was printed for inclusion as the frontispiece in the portfolio *Domestic Architecture in Rural France*. Each portfolio contains a proof of the print.

254. *Street Scene, Woebley*

The print was reproduced to illustrate the book *Tudor Homes of England*, page 145.

255. *A Windmill*

The print was made to illustrate editions of the book *Tudor Homes of England*. In the deluxe edition of fifty volumes, each one contains a proof of the print as a second frontispiece in addition to a proof of the etching No. 252, *The City Cross, Winchester*. In another edition of the book as well as this one, a reproduction of the print *A Windmill* appears on page 55.

256. *General Washington Saying Farewell to His Officers in Fraunces Tavern, New York*
The plate was engraved and an edition printed for inclusion in the portfolio *The Bicentennial Pageant of George Washington*, issued in 1932 by the George Washington Association to commemorate the two hundredth anniversary of his birth. The portfolio, also called *The George Washington Memorial Association Portfolio*, contains twenty prints portraying episodes in the life of George Washington, interpreted by Samuel Chamberlain and nineteen other well-known American graphic artists. The plates for many of these prints, including the one by Chamberlain, were printed in London by Henry Carling, although some plates were printed by the artists themselves. All proofs for this portfolio were printed on specially designed rag paper, handmade at Head Mill, Maidstone, England, and imprinted with George Washington's initials and coat of arms. A few proofs were printed from each plate before it was steel-faced. Following the printing of the edition, each plate was canceled and gold-faced.

257. *Butcher Row, Coventry*
A first state of two proofs was printed. The edition was printed for inclusion as the frontispiece in a deluxe edition of the book *This Realm, This England*. Each volume of this edition contains a proof of the print. The plate was found in the artist's studio after his death.

At the request of George Macy, president and founder of the Limited Editions Club, the twelve plates listed below were engraved by the artist and hand-printed by Charles Furth's shop in New York City, New York, to illustrate two special editions of the autobiography *The Education of Henry Adams*. Each volume of the edition published for the Limited Editions Club contains original prints from each of the twelve plates. Reproductions of each of the twelve prints illustrate the edition published for The Heritage Press, New York, 1942.

258. *The Adams Mansion, Quincy*
259. *The Harvard Yard, Cambridge*
260. *The Houses of Parliament, London*
261. *Mont-Saint-Michel*
262. *Mount Vernon Street, Boston*
263. *The North Porch of the Virgin of Chartres, a Vista*
264. *The Steps of Ara Coeli, Rome*
265. *The Town of Chartres*
266. *The Transept of the Cathedral of Notre Dame, Paris.*
267. *The Wadsworth House, Cambridge*
268. *Wenlock Abbey, Shropshire*
269. *Winter Evening on Beacon Street, Boston*

258. *The Adams Mansion, Quincy*
A first state of three proofs was printed.

259. *The Harvard Yard, Cambridge*
Two states of three proofs each were printed.

261. *Mont-Saint-Michel*
A partially engraved plate, described in the appendix "Unfinished Plates," entry "E," depicts a horizontal design of the same subject.

262. *Mount Vernon Street, Boston*
A second state of two proofs was printed. No records have been found of other states.

263. *The North Porch of the Virgin of Chartres, a Vista*
A second state of three proofs was printed. No records have been found of other states.

265. *The Town of Chartres*
A first state of four proofs was printed. A partially engraved plate, described in the appendix "Unfinished Plates," entry "D," depicts a different view of the same subject.

270. *The Tontine Crescent, Franklin Place, Boston*
The plate was engraved for presentation to the Iconographic Society of Boston and was referred to by the artist as *The Boston Library Plate* and as *The Club of Odd Volumes Plate* in correspondence during March 1928 with Charles D. Childs. The print depicts an area of the building designed by Charles Bulfinch where rooms were used by the Boston Library Society during the first half of the nineteenth

century. See page 58 in the book *Boston, A Topographical History*, by Walter Muir Whitehill, The Belknap Press of Harvard University Press, Cambridge, Massachusetts, 1959. The Iconographics Society was formed by a group of Boston gentlemen and included some members of the Club of Odd Volumes.

271. *Hospital Santa Cruz, Toledo*
The plate was engraved for presentation to The Print Club of Rochester, Rochester, New York, and was found in the artist's studio after his death.

272. *Mediterranean Village, Villefranche-sur-Mer*
The print is listed by the above title in the appendix "Published Etchings, Drypoints and Lithographs, and Commissioned Prints" in the artist's autobiography, *Etched in Sunlight*; is called *A Mediterranean Village* in a broadside printed by the Munson Gallery, New Haven, Connecticut; and was reproduced over the title *The Harbor, Villefranche-sur-Mer* in the book *France Will Live Again*, page 112. The print also has been referred to as *The Munson Plate*. It was presented by the Munson Gallery Print Club as its fourth annual offering to members. The plate, which had been engraved directly from nature, was printed in Paris by Edmond Rigal and was canceled after the edition was printed.

273. *Early Morning Market, Senlis*
The plate was engraved for presentation to the Society of American Etchers, renamed the Society of American Graphic Artists. The plate remained in their possession.

274. *The King Hooper Mansion*
The edition was donated to the Marblehead Arts Association of Marblehead, Massachusetts, to be sold for the benefit of the association.

275. *Summer Shadows*
A first state of a single proof, a second state of two proofs, and a third state of a single proof were printed. The print was reproduced, and an edition of three hundred copies was printed by The Meriden Gravure Company, Meriden, Connecticut. The edition of reproductions was copyrighted by the Marblehead Arts Association and was titled *Hooper Street*. The reproductions have the same dimensions as the original drypoint *Summer Shadows*. A soft-ground etching with the title *Hooper Street* is described in entry No. 201. A reproduction by The Meriden Gravure Company of the drypoint No. 123, *Summer Street, Marblehead*, also is named *Summer Shadows*. The plate, which had been engraved directly from nature, was found in the artist's studio after his death.

276. *Harbor Side, Friendship, Maine*
Three states of a single proof each were printed. No records of a fourth state have been found, but fifth and sixth states of six proofs each are indicated. The plate was engraved for presentation to the Chicago Society of Etchers, Chicago, Illinois.

277. *Old Nassau Hall, Princeton*
The plate was engraved for presentation to the Princeton Print Club, Princeton, New Jersey.

278. *Doorway of the Harvard Club, Boston*
The print was reproduced over the above title in the artist's autobiography, *Etched in Sunlight*, page 143, but is listed by the title *The Front Door* in the appendix "Published Etchings, Drypoints and Lithographs, and Commissioned Prints" of the same book. The plate, which had been printed and published for the Harvard Club of Boston, Massachusetts, was found in the artist's studio after his death.

279. *Harvard Hall.*
One of three working proofs is inscribed "Third state, only proof." Records of other states have not been found. The print is listed by the above title in the appendix "Published Etchings, Drypoints and Lithographs, and Commissioned Prints" in the artist's autobiography, *Etched in Sunlight*. The title *The Great Hall* has been written on some proofs. The plate, which had been printed and published for the Harvard Club of Boston, Massachusetts, was found in the artist's studio after his death.

280. *Jacquemart, Moulins*
Three states of a single proof each as well as a single trial proof were printed. The plate was engraved for presentation to the Rockford Print Club, Rockford, Illinois.

281. *Barnegat Cottage, Marblehead*

Two states of a single proof each were printed. The plate was engraved for presentation to the print club Friends of Contemporary Prints, Marblehead, Massachusetts.

282. *Saugus Ironworks*

Two states of a single proof each were printed. The plate, which had been commissioned by the Saugus Ironworks Association, Saugus, Massachusetts, was found in the artist's studio after his death.

283. *Continental Illinois Bank and Trust Company*

The print was commissioned by the officers and trustees of the Continental Illinois Bank and Trust Company, Chicago, Illinois.

284. *Bank of New York and Trust Company*

The print was commissioned by the officers and trustees of the Bank of New York and Trust Company, New York City, New York.

285. *Memorial Chapel*

In many of the artist's records, as well as in the list of published prints in the artist's autobiography, *Etched in Sunlight*, the print is titled *Memorial Chapel, Nashville, Tennessee*. However, the subject of the print has been identified conclusively as the Duncan Memorial Chapel in Floydsburg, Kentucky, a hamlet near Crestwood, Kentucky. The print was commissioned by Mr. A. E. Duncan, builder of the chapel. Mr. Duncan did not offer the proofs for sale, but gave them to friends and relatives. The plate was found in the artist's studio after his death.

286. *First National Bank Building of Boston*

Three states of two proofs each were printed. The print was commissioned by the officers and trustees of the First National Bank of Boston.

Books and Portfolios Written or Illustrated by Samuel Chamberlain

Beauport (1951). Hastings House, Publishers, Incorporated, New York. (Text and captions by Paul Hollister.)

Behold Williamsburg (1947). Hastings House.

The Berkshires (1956). Hastings House.

Beyond New England Thresholds (1938). Hastings House.

The Book of Boston, Volume I: *The Colonial Period* (1960). Hastings House. (Text by Marjorie Drake Ross.)

The Book of Boston, Volume II: *The Federal Period* (1961). Hastings House. (Text by Marjorie Drake Ross.)

The Book of Boston, Volume III: *The Victorian Period* (1964). Hastings House. (Text by Marjorie Drake Ross.)

Boston Landmarks (1946). Hastings House. (Text by Mark A. DeWolfe Howe.)

The Boston Massacre (1970). Hastings House. (Photographic illustrations only. Text by Harry Hansen.)

Bouquet de France (1952). Gourmet Distributing Corporation, New York.

Bouquet de France (1957). Gourmet Distributing Corporation. (Revised edition.)

Bouquet de France (1966). Gourmet Distributing Corporation. (New edition.)

Bouquet de France (1984). Hastings House. (Reprinted with introduction by Julia Child.)

British Bouquet (1963). Gourmet Distributing Corporation.

Cape Ann Through the Seasons (1953). Hastings House.

Cape Cod (1953). Hastings House.

Cape Cod in the Sun (1937). Hastings House.

The Chamberlain Sampler of American Cooking (1961). Hastings House. (Photographic illustrations. Text by Narcissa G. Chamberlain and Narcisse Chamberlain.)

The Chamberlain Selection of New England Rooms, 1639–1863 (1972). Hastings House. (With Narcissa G. Chamberlain.)

Churches of Old New England (1947). The Macmillan Company, New York. (Text by George Francis Marlowe.)

Clémentine in the Kitchen (1943). Gourmet Incorporated in cöoperation with Hastings House. (Published under the pen name of Phineas Beck.)

The Coast of Maine (1956). Thomas Y. Crowell Company, New York. (Photographic illustrations only. Text by Louise Dickinson Rich.)

The Coast of Maine (1970). Thomas Y. Crowell Company. (Photographic illustrations only. Text by Louise Dickinson Rich. Updated edition.)

Domestic Architecture in Rural France (1928). Portfolio published by Architectural Book Publishing Company, New York.

Domestic Architecture in Rural France (1981). Architectural Book Publishing Company. (Revised trade edition.)

The Education of Henry Adams (1942). The Limited Editions Club, Boston. (Etched illustrations only.)

Etched in Sunlight (1968). Boston Public Library, Boston.

Étude Historique de la Cuisine Française (1977). Taishukan Shoten, Tokyo. (Some etched and photographic illustrations only. Text by Shizuo Tsuji.)

Ever New England (1944). Hastings House. (Introduction by Donald Moffat.)

Fair Harvard (1948). Harvard University Press,

Cambridge, Massachusetts, and Hastings House. (Introduction and captions by Donald Moffat.)

Fair Is Our Land (1942). Hastings House. (Introduction by Donald Moffat.)

The Flavor of France, Volume I (1960). Hastings House. (Text by Narcissa G. Chamberlain and Narcisse Chamberlain.)

The Flavor of France, Volume II (1964). Hastings House. (Text by Narcissa G. Chamberlain and Narcisse Chamberlain.)

The Flavor of France (1969). Hastings House. (Combined collection of Volumes I and II. Text by Narcissa G. Chamberlain and Narcisse Chamberlain.)

The Flavor of France (1978). Hastings House. (Revised combined collection of Volumes I and II, 1969. Text by Narcissa G. Chamberlain and Narcisse Chamberlain.)

The Flavor of Italy (1965). Hastings House. (Text by Narcissa G. Chamberlain and Narcisse Chamberlain.)

Forty Acres (1949). Hastings House. (Text by James Lincoln Huntington.)

France Will Live Again (1940). Hastings House. (Introduction by Donald Moffat.)

French Menus for Parties (1968). Hastings House. (Photographic illustrations only. Text by Narcissa G. Chamberlain and Narcisse Chamberlain.)

Frontier of Freedom (1952). Hastings House. (With Henry N. Flynt.)

Gloucester and Cape Ann (1938). Hastings House.

Historic Boston in Four Seasons (1938). Hastings House.

Historic Cambridge in Four Seasons (1942). Hastings House.

Historic Connecticut (1944). Grosset and Dunlap, New York. (Original copyright 1934. Text by Marguerite Allis.)

Historic Deerfield: Houses and Interiors (1965). Hastings House. (With Henry N. Flynt.)

Historic Salem in Four Seasons (1938). Hastings House.

Holiday of a Cook (1981). Kamakura Shobo, Tokyo. (Etched and graphic illustrations. Text by Shizuo Tsuji.)

Invitation to Boston (1947). M. Barrows and Company, New York. (Text by Agnes C. Lyons.)

Italian Bouquet (1958). Gourmet Distributing Corporation.

Lexington and Concord (1939). Hastings House.

Lexington and Concord in Color (1970). Hastings House. (Introduction and text by Stewart Beach.)

Longfellow's New England (1972). Hastings House. (Text by Harry Hansen.)

Longfellow's Wayside Inn (1938). Hastings House.

Martha's Vineyard (1941). Hastings House.

Monticello, Home of Thomas Jefferson (1957). Hastings House. (Photographic illustrations only. Text by Randle Bond Truett.)

Mont Saint-Michel and Chartres (1957). Limited Editions Club printing of Henry Adams' text. (Photographic illustrations only.)

Mount Vernon, Virginia: An Illustrated Handbook (1947). The Mount Vernon Ladies Association of the Union, Mount Vernon, Virginia. (Photographic illustrations only.)

Mystic Seaport (1959). Hastings House.

Nantucket (1939). Hastings House.

Nantucket (1955). Hastings House. (New volume under title.)

New England in Color (1969). Hastings House. (Introduction and text by Stewart Beach.)

New England Doorways (1939). Hastings House.

The New England Image (1962). Hastings House.

New England Legends and Folklore (1967). Hastings House. (Photographic illustrations only. Edited by Harry Hansen.)

The New England Scene (1965). Hastings House.

North of Manhattan (1950). Hastings House. (Text by Harry Hansen.)

The Old Bay Paths (1942). Hastings House. (Text by George Francis Marlowe.)

Old Bridges of France (1925). Portfolio published by Press of The American Institute of Architects, New York. (Illustrated also by Louis C. Rosenberg and Pierre Vignal. Text by William Emerson and Georges Gromort.)

Old Marblehead (1940). Hastings House.

Old Marblehead (1975). Hastings House. (Revised and enlarged by Narcissa G. Chamberlain.)

Old Rooms for New Living (1953). Hastings House. (Text by Narcissa G. Chamberlain.)

Old Sturbridge Village (1951). Hastings House.

Open House in New England (1937). Stephen Daye Press, Brattleboro, Vermont.

Open House in New England (1948). Hastings House. (Revised edition.)

Portsmouth, New Hampshire (1940). Hastings House.

Princeton in Spring (1950). Princeton University Press, Princeton, New Jersey, and Hastings House.

Rockefeller Center: A Photographic Narrative (1947). Hastings House.

Salem Interiors (1950). Hastings House.

Six New England Villages (1948). Hastings House.

Sketches of Northern Spanish Architecture (1925). Portfolio published by Architectural Book Publishing Company.

A Small House in the Sun (1936). Hastings House.

A Small House in the Sun (1971). Hastings House. (Anniversary edition.)

Soft Skies of France (1953). Hastings House.

Southern Interiors of Charleston, South Carolina (1956). Hastings House. (With Narcissa G. Chamberlain.)

Springtime in Virginia (1947). Hastings House. (Introduction by Virginius Dabney.)

A Stroll Through Historic Salem (1969). Hastings House.

This Realm, This England (1941). Hastings House. (Introduction by Donald Moffat.)

Through France with a Sketchbook (1929). Robert M. McBride & Company, New York.

A Tour of Old Sturbridge Village (1955). Hastings House.

Tudor Homes of England (1929). Architectural Book Publishing Company. (With measured drawings by Louis Skidmore.)

Twelve Etchings of Yale (1934). Portfolio published by Yale University Press, New Haven, Connecticut.

The Use of Brick in French Architecture, Part One: The Midi (1935). Architectural Book Publishing Company. (Text by William Emerson and Georges Gromort.)

Vingt Lithographies du Vieux Paris (1924). Portfolio published by the artist, Paris.

Who Lived Here? (1952). Little, Brown Company, Boston. (Text by Mark A. DeWolfe Howe.)

The Yale Scene (1950). Yale University Press. (Introduction and captions by Robert D. French.)

Museums and Other Institutions Containing Prints by Samuel Chamberlain

Addison Gallery of American Art, Andover, Massachusetts

American Institute of Architects Foundation, The Octagon, Washington, D.C.

Art Institute of Chicago, Chicago, Illinois

Bibliothèque Nationale, Paris, France

Birmingham Museum of Art, Birmingham, Alabama

College of Wooster Museum, Wooster, Ohio

Boston Public Library, The Wiggin Collection, Boston, Massachusetts

British Museum, London, England

Cleveland Museum of Art, Cleveland, Ohio

Dallas Museum of Fine Arts, Dallas, Texas

Essex Institute, Salem, Massachusetts

Evansville Museum of Arts and Science, Evansville, Indiana

Library of Congress, Washington, D.C.

Los Angeles County Museum of Art, Los Angeles, California

Metropolitan Museum of Art, New York City, New York

Museum of Fine Arts, Boston, Massachusetts

Nelson Gallery, Atkins Museum of Fine Arts, Kansas City, Missouri

New Britain Museum of American Art, New Britain, Connecticut

New York Public Library, New York City, New York

Norton Simon Museum of Art at Pasadena, Pasadena, California

Philadelphia Museum of Art, Philadelphia, Pennsylvania

Sheldon Memorial Art Gallery, University of Nebraska-Lincoln, Lincoln, Nebraska

Smith College Museum of Art, Northampton, Massachusetts

Toledo Museum of Art, Toledo, Ohio

University of Michigan Museum of Art, Ann Arbor, Michigan

University of Oregon Library, Eugene, Oregon

Vassar College Art Gallery, Poughkeepsie, New York

Victoria and Albert Museum, London, England

Wadsworth Atheneum, Hartford, Connecticut

APPENDIX V

Awards and Decorations

Croix de Guerre, an individual citation and a regimental citation, World War I, 1917

American Field Service Travelling Fellowship, 1923

First Honorable Mention, Paris Salon, 1925, No. 1, *A Sidestreet in Beauvais*,
No. 20, *The Fish Market, Chartres*

Guggenheim Memorial Fellowship, 1927

Bronze Medal, etchings, Paris Salon, 1928

Kate W. Arms Prize, Society of American Etchers Exhibition, 1933

John Taylor Arms Prize, Society of American Etchers Annual Exhibition, 1936,
No. 123, *Summer Street, Marblehead*

Voted most popular print at the New York World's Fair, 1940, No. 127, *Springtime in Salem*

Legion of Merit, United States of America, World War II, 1944

Bronze Star Medal, United States of America, World War II, 1945

American Institute of Architects' Fine Arts Gold Medal, 1947

Chevalier de la Légion d' Honneur, France, 1949

Annual Award, New England Society in the City of New York, 1955

Stella Della Solidarita Italiana, 1958

Certificate of Merit, National Academy of Design, New York City, June 1963

Trofeo Bologna, Gastronomic Prize from the City of Bologna, Italy, 1965

Master of Arts, Honorary, at Marlboro College, Vermont, 1968

Special Annual Award from the National Trust for Historic Preservation, 1972

APPENDIX VI

Memberships

American Academy of Arts and Sciences

American Institute of Architects, Honorary

American Institute of Interior Designers, Honorary

The American Society of the French Legion of Honor

The Boston Camera Club

The Boston Printmakers

Chicago Society of Etchers

Club of Odd Volumes, Boston, Massachusetts

The Colonial Society of Massachusetts

The Commanderie de Bordeaux, France

Confrèrie des Chevaliers du Tastevin, Nuits Saint Georges, Côtes d'Or, France

Marblehead Arts Association, Marblehead, Massachusetts

Marblehead Historical Society, Marblehead, Massachusetts

National Academy of Design, National Academician

Phi Delta Theta Fraternity

Photographic Society of America, Associate

The Print Club of Albany

Society of American Etchers, which has been renamed The Society of American Graphic Artists

Société de la Gravure Originale en Noir, Paris

Tavern Club, Boston

INDICES

Index of the Prints
by Location of the Subject

IDENTIFIED BY PRINT NUMBERS

IMAGINARY SETTINGS

Index of Titles of the Prints, with Print Numbers and Metric Measurements

359

General Index

INDEX OF NAMES MENTIONED ONLY

THE PRINTS OF SAMUEL CHAMBERLAIN, N.A. has been designed by Freeman Keith. The type is Linoterm Galliard, composed at The Stinehour Press, Lunenburg, Vermont. The photography, in 300-line-screen halftone from the original prints, and the presswork, in offset lithography, were done by The Meriden Gravure Company, Meriden, Connecticut. William Glick saw the book through the press. The paper is Mohawk Superfine Text, soft-white, eggshell finish. The endleaves are tan Curtis Tweedweave Text. Binding, by The Stinehour Press, is in Holliston Roxite cloth, gold-stamped.
The book is published in an edition
of one thousand copies.